SUFFOLK'S
HISTORIC FARMS

SUFFOLK'S
HISTORIC FARMS

by Peter Hopper

First published in Great Britain in 2004 by
The Breedon Books Publishing Company Limited
Breedon House, 3 The Parker Centre,
Derby, DE21 4SZ.

ISBN 1 85983 422 1

Printed and bound by Butler & Tanner,
Frome, Somerset, England.

Cover printing by Lawrence-Allen Colour Printers,
Weston-super-Mare, Somerset, England.

Contents

Acknowledgements

As seven of the eight farming estates featured in this book were also featured in my original weekly series on 100 family farms in Suffolk and North Essex, published in the *East Anglian Daily Times (EADT)* in the mid-1990s, I wish to thank the owners of those estates for providing further valuable information which could not be included in the newspaper series for reasons of limited space. In this context, I am particularly grateful to John and Pat Knock, and their son Christopher, who put their detailed family research work at my disposal.

In the case of Priory Farm, Preston St Mary, my thanks to Adrian Thorpe for the information which came via a number of speakers taking part in a historical farm open day for members of the Suffolk Farming and Wildlife Advisory Group (FWAG), which I was delighted to attend. The only estate not in the original series was Kentwell Hall, Long Melford, and a meeting with owner Patrick Phillips in the New Year of 2004 enabled me to use details of 16th-century farming at the hall.

In all other respects, second visits to the estates and further interviews with the owners provided a wealth of new information. I am therefore also grateful to Jack, Bill and Jane Kemball; David and Claire Barker; Stephen Wise, Philip Hope-Cobbold and Sir Edward Greenwell.

Thanks are also due to the *EADT* for allowing me to use some material from the newspaper series and for the use of recent photographs of Sir Edward Greenwell, taken by photographer Keith Mindham – PH.

Thanks are given by the author for the provision of the following items:
Drawings and some photographs of St John's Manor, Battisford.
Glemham Hall, The Walled Rose Garden, The Grand Staircase, The lock of Mary Tudor's hair and The Nursery, by Graham Portlock
Aerial photographs of Glemham Hall taken for Philip Hope-Cobbold
Mary Tudor, c.1514, St Mary's Church, Bury St Edmunds
Wedding portrait, Mary Tudor & Charles Brandon, The Marquess of Tavistock and Trustees of the Bedford Estate.

Dedication

To Bobbie, for many hours alone
during my preparation of this book

John Gummer, MP for Suffolk Coastal, lives at Winston Grange, near Debenham, Suffolk. He was Conservative Cabinet Minister in the governments of both Margaret Thatcher and John Major, and has a total of 16 years ministerial experience. As Minister of Agriculture, Fisheries & Food (1989–93), John was the first MAFF Minister to take seriously the effects of agriculture policy on wildlife and the countryside. As Environment Secretary (1993–97), he played a key role in the Convention on Climate Change meetings in Berlin and Geneva. Friends of the Earth described him as 'the best Environment Secretary we've ever had.'

Foreword

by John Gummer, MP for Suffolk Coastal

Suffolk is inconceivable without agriculture. It is farming that has shaped our landscape and made our history. Our glorious churches, Lavenham, Long Melford, Blythbrough and the rest speak of the wealth of the wool trade. It was Suffolk sheep that sustained the abbeys of Leiston, Sibton and Bury St Edmunds, and it was the farm traffic that created the road pattern that still spreads out from the Benedictine house at Bury. So too, it is to the grain trade that Halesworth owes its canal and Ipswich much of the strength of its port.

The great names in the agricultural industry are remembered in the places they helped to prosperity. Smythe's drills in Peasenhall, Garretts in Leiston, and Ransomes in Ipswich. Yet it is the thousands of unnamed farmers who have most affected the Suffolk of today. They created our landscape, from unenclosed greens like Wingfield to the prairie fields of Tannington and along the Bungay straight. They irrigated and fertilised the light land of the coast and Smythe, Ransome, and Garrett enabled them to cultivate the heavy clays inland.

Yet it is the Suffolk Trinity that is still most evocative of our agricultural past. Although the Suffolk sheep has remained the most successful, the distinctive Red Poll has not lost its appeal to the specialist and its meat is well represented in today's farmers' markets, particularly in Woodbridge and Easton Farm Park. Even so, for me, the Suffolk Punch stands best for Suffolk. That wonderful, careful strength, its plaited mane, broad back, and handsome head – the Punch is a workhorse with true nobility. Saving the stud at Hollesley Bay has guaranteed its future and is a tribute we all owed to our inheritance.

What a canvas this is. From the reed harvesting and the grazing meadows of the Blythe to the horses exercising over the downs at Newmarket and from Constable's rural idyll in the Dedham Vale to Bernard Matthews's turkeys in Holton, Peter Hopper has the most varied and complex story to tell. Long admired as a sage and objective agricultural journalist, this is his tribute to the farmers and farm workers who formed our landscape and still look after our land.

Preface

'Custodians of the Countryside'

Special to Suffolk – fine examples of the county's 'livestock trinity' of Red Poll cattle, Suffolk sheep and the famous Suffolk Punch, believed to be the oldest heavy horse breed in the world. This photograph was taken in the mid-1990s at Roger Clark's Weylands Farm, Stoke by Nayland.

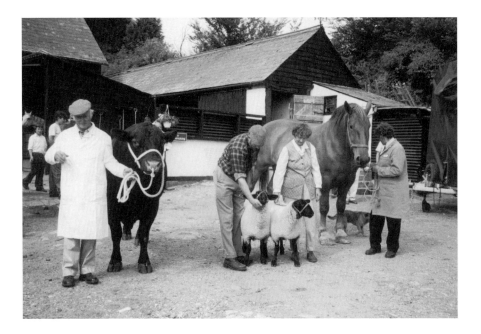

Farmers and landowners use a particularly apt phrase with immense pride to describe what they are and what they do – 'Custodians of the Countryside'. It recognises, and is accepted by all, that guardianship of a Blessed Plot of native soil, however large or small, is but a temporary thing. People before them tilled the same plot of land with equal care, but needed more manpower than is required in the 21st century. When less able because of age and fitness, they hand over the task to younger generations, sometimes to other families, to continue the cycle of renewal that, in essence, has been unaltered for centuries.

At the very heart of farm life is the family. Transfer of responsibility has largely been through the continuity of kinship, the handing over of custodianship from father to sons, and sometimes to daughters too. The ties that bind flesh and blood of succeeding generations are nowhere felt more strongly than in the traditional farming areas of rural England.

I chose the phrase of the farming community, 'Custodians of the Countryside', to begin a weekly series of articles for the *East Anglian Daily Times*, a regional morning newspaper, on family farming in East

Anglia, an area where I worked as an agricultural journalist for almost three decades, and have continued to live in since retirement from daily journalism in Suffolk. The phrase became the headline for the first article, and set the tone for an award-winning series which ran for more than two years, and featured some 100 well-known families in the counties of Suffolk and north Essex.

On some of these farms, I found three generations of families working in perfect harmony. These are the people who take particular pride in the heritage that has kept them producing wholesome food for our nation, in spite of the vagaries of weather and a constantly changing political climate, neither of which they are able to control.

Most of these farmers like nothing better than to plough back profits into their enterprises. I asked one what he would do if he won a lot of money. He thought for a moment and then replied, with a twinkle in his eye: 'I would invest it in the farm – until it was all gone.' His whimsical comment spoke volumes for the precarious nature of farming in any age. He is not alone in finding it difficult to continue traditional patterns of East Anglian farming within the ever-changing framework of the European Union's Common Agricultural Policy.

The series was too large in scope to condense into a single book, so I decided to concentrate mainly on the fascinating historical aspects of a small number of holdings, enlarging on the detail through further research and interviews with present custodians – the bedrock farmers and family members who really care for the region's rural environment.

CHAPTER 1

St John's Manor Farm, Battisford

Give me here John Baptist's head in a charger
– The Bible, Matthew 14: 8

An introduction to 1,000 years of history

The moated St John's Manor Farm, deep in the mid-Suffolk countryside at Battisford, near Stowmarket, has existed since Saxon times, the first owner being Sir Roger de Chandos, who is mentioned in the Domesday Book of 1086.

The present Elizabethan farmhouse is occupied by retired farmer John Knock and his wife, Pat. Their son, Christopher, a prominent Suffolk farmer and Project Director of an organisation which has helped thousands of other regional farmers, is responsible for farming the manor's 220 acres on a part-time basis.

When I first visited the farm in 1996, I was given the warmest of welcomes by the family, and remember wishing that the day had been colder, for I would have appreciated more the log fire burning brightly in the large fireplace which has a carving of the head of St John the Baptist set into the brickwork above.

My second visit, in late spring of 2003, was to add much more to the story I had written for the *East Anglian Daily Times*. This time, the fruits of further research by the Knock family, and descendants of the Lingwood

family, occupants in an earlier age, were laid out on the huge dining table in front of that same fireplace. The results of painstaking research by many people – written accounts and catalogued lists of previous occupants of Manor Farm, photographs and diagrams, the results of exterior archaeological digs (official and unofficial) and extensive interior investigations of the house structure – were placed before me. To my surprise, I was invited to take it all away with me and sift through the evidence uncovered over many years.

The story of almost 1,000 years of history of St John's Manor Farm is a truly remarkable one, faithfully researched, as always, by people who have the curiosity and patience to dive into the past to discover the living of past generations who occupied the same patch of earth in these islands. The results of their investigations are hugely enjoyable.

Pat related that in 1981 Dr Kenneth Nicholls-Palmer, a Knight of Justice of the Order of St John of Jerusalem, contacted the local clergyman, and at the time her family had no knowledge that they would be able to live at Manor Farm. But when, in 1984, they knew they would indeed be living there, they got in touch with Nicholls-Palmer, and later had two study days with him.

'We had a lovely time,' said Pat, 'We were invited to an investiture of the Order. It was just like those at Buckingham Palace, except that they use a little black cushion and not a crimson one, and the occasion was to be a real eye-opener. Knights still appoint their squires, that's how the ceremony finished, but they went through all the awards for the St John Ambulance personnel, who do a lot of training in industry.'

Pat added: 'A lot of people wonder how this farm came into the Knights' possession, and it is generally believed it was because either the life of the person concerned [the owner-occupier], or one of his family, was saved by the Knights Hospitallers during the Crusades.'

John and Pat's *History of St John's Manor*, published in booklet form in 1997, and to which I will refer extensively, was penned just 11 years after they took possession of the property. It was a homecoming for John, who was born there, and a delight to Pat for its historical association.

This is their fascinating story, and I am pleased to tell it the way they wish it to be told. It begins with an unanswerable question: 'How does one dispose of a thousand years in two sentences?' The couple had learned from recent finds that the Romans were very near the area in the first and third century. The curtain then drops and does not lift again until the 10th century when there were two Saxon manors in Battisford, which changed hands after the Norman Conquest.

Over the years of the Anglo-Saxon period, the social structure of the population had evolved from the 'kindred' concept, where the family was the responsible unit, to a landowning nobility with sub-tenants. 'So the framework for our manor was in being in 1066 and went forward in new ownership but with much of its customs and practises little changed,' say the Knocks.

Copinger, in his *Manors of Suffolk*, lists the holder of Battisford Manor as Aluric, a freeman, with one carucate. A carucate was reckoned as the

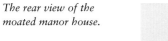

The rear view of the moated manor house.

amount of land that could be ploughed by a team of oxen in one year – an area that varied from 60 to 120 acres, according to the heaviness of the land.

Attached to the manor were eight bordars (copyholders with small amounts of land), two plough teams with demesne (which would have been oxen), a plough team belonging to the men, six acres of meadow and a wood for 20 hogs. There was also half a church with 20 acres. The other half of the church went with the other manor.

In 1086 the Domesday Survey listed Roger de Chandos as holding the Manor from Hugh de Montford and the King. Both these Norman nobles were rewarded by King William after the Battle of Hastings. De Montford had added to his manor in an exchange with St Augustine's land, and the present owners speculate that this could also have involved the nearby priory at Great Bricett.

The couple say they must assume that for the next 60 years or so, the manor followed the usual course at the time, of being run by a reeve responsible to an absentee landlord. Sometime in the middle of the 12th century a great change took place. The manor became the property of the Order of St John of Jerusalem and served as its headquarters in Suffolk.

The Order of St John – the Knights Hospitallers

Long before the Crusades took place, Christian travellers took to the Holy Land, facing a long and dangerous journey through Europe by land and sea. Robbers on the land and pirates at sea attacked them, or else they fell ill from some disease or just sheer weariness.

By the time of the Crusades, there was an established hostel run by monks caring for the sick and injured. Their good work came to the attention of Pope Paschal II, who formally recognised them as a religious order, the Knights Hospitallers, in 1113.

The Christian Order of Templars was formed about this time (1119), and theirs was a fighting role. The Hospitallers acquired an ancient Greek monastery dedicated to St John the Baptist, who thereafter became the patron saint of their Order.

One of the Knights who lived at Battisford Manor was Sir Giles Russell, who commissioned a terracotta plaque of St John the Baptist's head on a charger, with two supporting angels. This is the one over the fireplace in the dining room and would originally have been in the gatehouse to the Commandery. A Commandery was the headquarters of the Order – generally there was one in each country.

The carving of the head of St John the Baptist on a charger.

John and Pat Knock with the carving of the head of St John the Baptist from the chimney in the dining room of the manor house. They arranged for it to be restored and replaced.

During their study time at St John's Gate, Clerkenwell, London, the Order's headquarters, John and Pat were able to make a list of some of the commanders that had been in charge at Battisford. The list is not complete and also contains the names of some Knights about whom little is known. These, in the following list, have an asterisk by their names:

1189	Brian of London
1221	Richard of Battisford
1338	Richard de Bachesworth*
1358	Thomas Madeston
1415	Henry Corbet
1445	Richard Topshill
1450	Thomas Davenport*
1470	Henry Naylor
1475	William Weston*
1480	Henry Halley*
1489	James Alston
1500	Adam Chetwode*
1507	Thomas Golyns
1510	Thomas Sheffield
1523	Giles Russell*
1527	William Tyrell

An inventory of all the Knights' estates throughout the country was carried out in 1338, when Richard de Bachesworth was Commander and Brother William Conegrave the other Knight in residence. The accounts are very detailed, but they show that hospitality to travellers was regular. Wheat was a large household expense and oats amounted to £7 4s, a sum which these days would equate to well over £4,000. It was reckoned that 'fish, flesh and other necessities for the kitchen at three shillings per week' amounted to £7 10s. Ale was not forgotten and cost £5 4s annually.

The Knights of St John eventually held property in nearly 50 parishes in Suffolk, the most important being at Coddenham and Mellis. After the dissolution of the Templars in 1312, they acquired a house, chapel and other property at Dunwich and also land at Gislingham and Thurlow.

Thomas Davenport, one time Commander at Battisford, was mentioned in the records when he left Battisford to go to Shingay in

*Still in good condition
– the paddle used by
the Knights of St John
to stir their ale.*

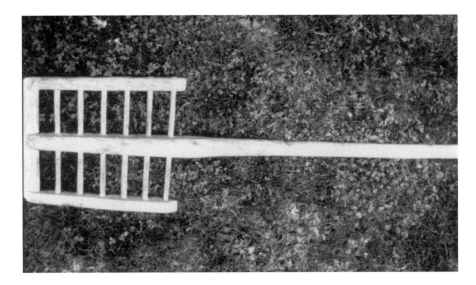

Cambridgeshire. John and Pat visited Shingay and found the remains of a moat enclosing some cattle.

William Weston, at Battisford in 1475, rose to be the last Grand Prior of the Order in England in 1527. After Henry Halley lived in Battisford, he was called to service in Rhodes, where he was killed by the Turks during the first siege of Rhodes in 1480. Adam Chetwode's name is mentioned in connection with the rebuilding of the Commandery after a terrible fire in the late 1400s. Some of the charred beams can still be seen in the present roof.

Apart from the plaque of St John the Baptist, Sir Giles Russell also commissioned another terracotta plaque of his coat-of-arms. When rediscovered in the cellar during the house repairs of 1984–85, the date of 1529 was deciphered. This probably meant that he was at Battisford at the same time as William Tyrell. The plaque was restored by donations received from the Order at St John's Gate, the Suffolk Council of St John, Dr Kenneth Nicholls-Palmer and Mr George Stennett. Pat Knock provided the remainder.

'This restored work has been placed in the side of the main chimney-piece and provides another link with someone who lived, prayed and worked at the Manor,' say John and Pat. Prayers and farming, as well as hospitality, filled the days for the household in times past. The Knights, although not monks, took the vows of poverty, obedience and chastity.

The present parish church of St Mary was built during the Knights' time in Battisford. They were responsible for appointing alternate priests and had other duties in connection with the care of the church fabric.

All the members of the Order received some nursing training, and in

The terracotta coat of arms discovered in the cellar.

Rhodes and Malta in particular they were called on to fight and protect their hospitals. Henry VIII dissolved the Order, along with all other Catholic monastic institutions, and confiscated its estates. Some of these the King retained, while some were sold.

The Gresham family – Tudor incumbents of St John's Manor

John and Pat Knock next turn their attention to the Greshams, a Norfolk family who have a village named after them in the north of that county. However, the branch of the family relevant to this story lived in a large house at Holt, and their home became Greshams School. It was here that the four sons of John and Alice Gresham were born: William, Thomas, Richard and John. The third son, Richard, became a London merchant

The Order of St John in England

1099   Land was first given to the Hospitallers in England after the First Crusade.

*c.*1144 Henry Jordan de Bricett, a Suffolk man, gave an area of land, just outside the City wall of London, on which to build the Priory of England at Clerkenwell. Part of the church and the entrance gate still exist as the present headquarters of the Order. The Grand Prior of England ranked as the premier Baron of England with the title Lord Prior of St John. Branches were established in Ireland, Scotland and Wales, but although they were within the Priory of England, they had a large degree of independence.

1185   The Priory Church was consecrated by Heraclius, Patriarch of Jerusalem at the same time as the Temple Church built by the Knights Templar. The two churches were similar and the round-naved Temple Church near Fleet Street still stands.

1312   The Priory of England inherited additional property at the dissolution of the Knights Templar.

1338   The Prior Philip de Thame ordered a return to be made of all the Hospitallers' property. The Priory included 90 manors organised into 36 commanderies or preceptories, including the property previously held by the Templars. The report of Philip de Thame gives many interesting details of the Suffolk Commandery of Battisford.

1381   During the Peasants' Revolt, much of the Priory at Clerkenwell was burnt. Of the original 12th-century buildings, only the Norman crypt, with its fine vaulted roof, remains.

1540   The Statute of Suppression, issued by Henry VIII, resulted in the dissolution of the Order of St John. The English Tongue survived in Malta with a small number of Knights. The English Knights gradually died and the post of Prior of England was filled by other nationalities.

1831   The Order of St John in England declared itself an independent entity.

1882   The Ophthalmic Hospital of St John was opened in Jerusalem. This hospital and the St John Ambulance Brigade are the two principal charitable foundations of the Order of St John today.

1887   The Order founded the St John Ambulance Brigade to train the public in First Aid.

1888   Queen Victoria gave her consent to the Royal Charter of Incorporation to the Order. It was given the title 'The Grand Priory of the Order of the Hospitallers of St John of Jerusalem in England,' and the Queen became its Sovereign Head.

1922   Cadet Divisions, attached to the Ambulance and Nursing Divisions, were formed. They consisted of two sections: Senior 16–18 years, Junior 11–16 years.

before becoming an Alderman, Sheriff and eventually Lord Mayor of London. He also had Battisford connections.

Following the departure of the Knights Hospitallers, ousted by Henry VIII during the Dissolution of the Monasteries, the property was taken over by the Crown. In 1543, it was allocated to Sir Andrew Judde, who supposedly did not have much interest in the manor, for in 1544 the ownership was transferred to Sir Richard Gresham. Soon after this Gresham also bought the other manor – Battisford Hall.

In his work in London, Sir Richard was concerned that the merchants, who assembled twice a day in Lombard Street to transact business, had no roof over their heads, and thought that they should have a significant building similar to the one that graced Antwerp. However, it was left to his son Thomas, who had the means as well as the inclination, to construct London's first Exchange.

Thomas was Sir Richard's second son, and after attending Gonville College in Cambridge he joined his uncle, Sir John Gresham, in London. In 1543 Thomas was admitted to the Mercers Company. A year later he married Anne Ferneley, of West Creeting, near Needham Market. Besides visiting Antwerp as a merchant he became a royal agent to King Henry VIII. In modern times, say the Knocks, we would say that besides his other attributes he was a financial wizard, for he managed to clear the King's considerable debts.

When Queen Mary, a Catholic, came to the throne, Protestant Thomas was dismissed for a while, but when his successor failed at the job, he was reinstated. It was in Queen Elizabeth I's time that he gave his greatest service to the country. During his visits to the Continent he became aware of Philip of Spain's intentions and encouraged the surreptitious stockpiling of arms in the Tower of London to counter the threat of invasion.

Thomas also had a house at Rinzall (now Ringshall) and this, together with his property at St John's Manor, included much oak woodland. Vast forests still covered much of England in the 16th century, but today Battisford Tye (common) is arable land with houses around the edge of what was common land. Having obtained permission to build the London Exchange, a vast number of workmen were sent to fell the oaks and form them into timber frames. In living memory the whereabouts of the remains of some of the sawpits were known. It is said that the proposed building was framed up on the Tye before being shipped to London.

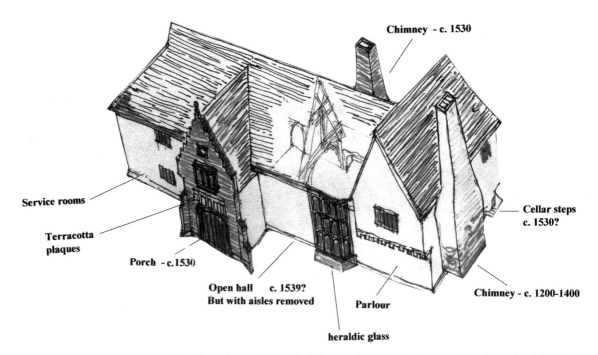

Chimney - c. 1530

Service rooms

Terracotta
plaques

Porch - c.1530

Open hall   c. 1539?
But with aisles removed

heraldic glass

Parlour

Chimney - c. 1200-1400

Cellar steps
c. 1530?

*A conjectural view of
St John's Manor
House, c.1530,
illustrating the
fragments of the
building that remain.*

The first foundation brick was laid by Thomas Gresham in 1566 and the building was completed by the end of the next year. Queen Elizabeth opened the Exchange, conferred on it the title Royal, and gave the man who had brought his father's idea to fruition a knighthood – he was now Sir Thomas Gresham.

In the years after the Knights' departure from Battisford it is thought that the Manor House lay empty. One theory is that it was rebuilt, using some of the last Commandery's timber, together with oak left from the Royal Exchange. It is not clear whether Sir Richard's widow or Sir Thomas's agent lived at the manor.

In 1547, Sir Thomas founded a college in London. Gresham College became a public school, virtually the first in London. He also made charitable bequests, including some almshouses close to his mansion in the parish of St Peter-the-Poor. Sir Thomas died in London on 21 November 1579 at the age of 60. At his death he was said to be the wealthiest commoner in England.

St John's Manor in the 17th and 18th century

The last Gresham to hold the Ringshall and Battisford estates was William, the son of Sir John Gresham, who sold it to John Barker in 1609. In turn it was passed on to Sir Robert Barker and so to Sir Thomas Barker. The latter sold the manor to Thomas Knapp, an Ipswich merchant, who left it to his two daughters, Katherine and Martha. John

Arnold married Katherine and bought the other half of the manor from Martha's husband, Robert Knowlys.

By 1693 we read of Nicholas Bacon, whose family seat was at Shrubland Hall. In 1707 Sir Samuel Barnardiston, a member of an ancient Suffolk family, is mentioned. As a younger man he was a staunch Roundhead and could have been responsible for the 'nickname' bestowed on his party by Queen Henrietta Maria. He went on to make a fortune in the Levant and eventually welcomed Charles II back to the throne so warmly that he was knighted!

Then followed several generations of Studds. In 1715 Samuel Studd is mentioned followed by his father, another Samuel, and then John Studd in 1777. His son, John Lynch Studd, served in the forces of the East India Company, which may account for the large amount of broken blue and white crockery found in the moat. The Studds were related to the Harwood family – Thomas Studd Harwood lived at Battisford Hall.

When Matthew and Job Raikes bought the manor in 1795, it was mentioned that an Edward Griggs Ward was farming 95 acres of it. The Raikes family, who came from London, paid a lump sum to extinguish the land tax. They added several fields, purchased as common allotment when the Tye was enclosed in 1812. One of these fields, at the east end of the Tye, is now called Jackaman's Loss. Jackaman, who lived in a cottage by Tye Gate farm, lost the grazing and shelter for his donkey on that corner of the Tye when it was ploughed.

The Knock family possess an estate map showing that William Matthew Raikes was farming 360 acres in 1812, but the outlying parts of the farm were sold off over the next 100 years. William Raikes retained the lordship of the manor after the farm was bought by the Lingwood family.

The Lingwood family – and a remarkable coincidence

Says Pat Knock: 'In the village in Surrey where I spent my first 18 years, lived a family who had an orchard, and during the war kept a large flock of hens. Mrs Liddell was a member of our Young Farmers' Club Advisory Committee when I was the Club Secretary. In 1953, when I married, she told me she had relations living in Suffolk, but the name Battisford was never mentioned.

'When staying with friends at Southwold in 1985, Molly Liddell paid a visit to the manor to photograph the house. We were still living in part of Battisford Hall then and she departed telling Edith Aggas she would write to John. Imagine my surprise when I saw the signature on her letter. In 1992 we met at the manor and gave her a tour of the house and garden, and Molly left the history of the Lingwood family with us. Sadly, she died the next year, but her son, Edward, has passed the history down to me, documents I feel honoured to possess.'

The story of the Lingwoods to which Pat refers, is contained in a substantial file within a cardboard box which my wife called an 'Aladdin's cave'. Although in my possession for only a short while, I felt immensely privileged to look through its very detailed pages. The compiler of this wonderful family record, Edith Wilson, refers to it as her 'labour of love for my nephew and nieces, my great-nephews and great-nieces.' There follows Pat Knock's precis of the Lingwood story:

Part of the transcription of the last will and testament of Robert Lingwood, 1528, by W.J.M. Lingwood.

In dei nom Amen / the second Daye of August / in the yer of our Lord god MCCCCCXXVIIJ I Robert Lynghood of Saynt Michaell in Rysmer beinge in good myend & hole remebrannce make my Last testamet & Wyll in this manr first I bequethe my soule to god allmightye & to or Ladye & all the holye Copeny in hevyne & my body to be buryed in the church of Saynte Michael of Rysm Imprmis I bequethe to the hyghe auter of Rysm for my tiths forgoten ij s Item I bequethe to Mutforthe hyghe auter vj d Item I bequethe to hensted hye auter viij d Item to gysloe hye auter vj d (Item to gysloe hye auter vj d.) Item I geve to the Reparcon of Rysm churche one ombe malte & one cobe wheat & vj d s viij d Item I give Nicholas my eldest son V mks sterlinge & a cowe & a Some of Barlye Item I geve Elyzabethe my Dowghter fyve mks & a cowe & a Seme of Barlye Item I geve Margery my Dowghter V mks & a cowe & a Seme of Barlye Item I geve Laurance my sone fyve mks a cowe & a seme of barlye Itm I geve Thomas my sone fyve mks & a cowe and a seme of Barlye Itm I geve Robert my sone v mks & a cowe & a seme of barlye Itm I gave the chyld that my wyffe is wt v mks a cowe & a seme of Barlye & all my chylder a fore or ehersyd to have ther bequest tht ther father have gevyne them at thage of xx ti yer Itm I will tht if ther Dye one of my chylder than yt the fyre mks to go to an honest prst to singe for me & my frendo in Rysmr churche & if ther Due toe or they on to

The Lingwood family's line of descent traces back to the early 16th century, and includes the last will and testament of one Robert Lyngwood, of Rushmere St Andrew, dated 1528. The document has been carefully transcribed by John (W.J.M.) Lingwood, of Barningham, near Bury St Edmunds.

The Lingwoods arrived at Battisford in 1827, on the marriage of Edward Lingwood (1797–1864) to Sarah Hayward (1804–1879), whose father was a miller in Needham Market. They were married in Barking Church. Over 17 years Edward and Sarah had 14 children. The eldest, another Edward, was born in 1828. He attended Eye Grammar School and started farming in Ashfield at the age of 20. Edward was a follower of the Essex and Suffolk Hunt and a keen and informed ornithologist. In modern terminology he was a 'twitcher', travelling long distances to hear and see rare species. He retired to Ipswich.

Born in 1829 were twins Thomas and Sarah. When she grew up, Sarah married a Dr Charles Cooper, who practised in Needham Market from 1864 to 1895 and was also a JP. Her son also became a doctor, as did her grandson – the father of Molly Liddell. Pat Knock's interest in this family thus becomes apparent. As a boy Thomas was friendly with John Knock of Rose Farm, and in the way that farmers did, they would meet at a meadow and lean on the gate and talk farming, and maybe religion. Thomas went as a young man to Shrubland House, Brockford, where he became a a real lover and breeder of horses. He once boasted that in 67 years he only missed the Woodbridge Horse Show three times. His garden was his hobby and he became noted for his roses in particular.

Although raised in a Church of England family, Thomas Lingwood became a member of the Plymouth Brethren and held services in his house. He later converted a barn and finally built a Gospel Hall on his land. He retired to Stonham Parva. As a girl, Sarah was interested in horses, but more for riding than breeding. She had many other interests and was among the first visitors to the Ipswich Museum when it opened in Arcade Street.

Fourth in the family was Henry, who trained in the corn milling industry in Devon. He is listed as a corn miller at Barking in 1855, and he was also a farmer. Sheep were his particular interest and he had one of the early flocks of Suffolk sheep, established in 1866 and listed in the first flock book of the Suffolk Sheep Society. Towards the end of his life, from 1882 until his death in 1906, he was agent to the Earl of Ashburnham, who owned the now demolished Barking Hall.

Nothing is known about Horace, but Septimus Robert married Ellen Mumford from Great Bricett Hall and emigrated to Canada. Here he called himself Robert S. Lingwood. Frederick died as a young man, but the Knocks know a little more about Walter Lingwood, who went to live in Barningham, where his descendants still live.

Sadly, the next two children died. Elizabeth was nine when she passed away and Arthur only three months old. They are buried in the east end of Battisford parish churchyard. The next son, Decimus, married but had no children. He lived for a while at Ashburnham Farm, Barking, during the time that his elder brother Henry was the Earl of Ashburnham's agent. Alice married and had four children, but little else is recorded about her. The 14th and last child of this large family was William. He went to Canada but later returned to England when his marriage broke up and he settled at Stowmarket.

The present Battisford Manor house has, on two sides, an outer wall of white brick, now grey with age. John and Pat are fairly sure that this was built by Edward Lingwood, and they say that it would have looked quite stunning new. 'In 1984', says Pat, 'we had to remove the south brick wall as it was pulling the half-timbered wall with it. My husband picked up one brick to examine it and to his surprise it was labelled "Fisons Stowmarket." They were certainly making bricks at the time the Lingwoods were living at the manor.'

In a directory of 1846, it was recorded that 'Edward Lingwood Esq. has a beautiful residence and pleasure grounds and is perpetual church warden.' Several of the evergreen and conifer trees planted by the Lingwoods are still in the garden, along with a very tall lime tree.

John and Pat are not sure when the Lingwoods left Battisford and retired to Stowmarket. However, they have some details about the Boby family who were next to live at the manor.

Boby, Larnach and Sturgeon – 19th-century custodians of St John's Manor

Charles Boby and his wife Mary were living in the Manor in the 1860s. What the present incumbents know of their farming comes from two farm diaries kept by a farm pupil named Thynne, whose comprehensive record of the year's activities in 1867-68 makes interesting reading.

The Knocks believe that the manor farm in those days was larger than it is now, but only one field name is mentioned – Upper Badley, then a grass layer. There were 21 workmen who included Boy Elijah,

St John's Manor, Battisford

Pre-conquest Saxon Manor	Aluric	
1086	Roger de Chandos	Domesday Survey
Circa 1150 Coddenham	Knights Hospitallers of St John	Land also held in Mellis &
1300	John de Accombe	Preceptors
	Richard de Bachesworth	
1400	William de Congreve	
	Henry Halley	Killed at Siege of Rhodes
	Thomas Davenport	
	Adam Chetwode	Rebuilt Manor after fire
	Giles Russell	Turcopolier
1500	William Tyrell	Last Preceptor
Dissolution of Monasteries by Henry VIII		
	Sir Richard Gresham	London Merchant
1600	Sir Thomas Gresham	Founder of Royal Exchange
	Sir Thomas Barker	
	Thomas Knapp	(Coat of arms in stained glass)
	John Arnold	Married Knapp's daughter
	Nicholas Bacon	Family seat at Shrubland Hall
1700	Sir Samuel Barnardiston	
	Samuel Studd	Married Elizabeth Fairfax
	Samuel Studd	
	John Studd	
	John Lynch Studd	East India Company
	Edward Griggs Ward	
1800	William Matthew Raikes	
	William Raikes	Farm map 1812
	Edward Lingwood	1844
	Charles Boby	1860
	Donald Larnach	1872
	Joseph Sturgeon	1885
	Herbert John Knock	1907
	John Herbert Knock	1916
1900	John Edward Knock & Joan Knock	1969

Boy Moyse, Boy Rose, Boy Laflin and Boy Battle. Up to seven plough teams are mentioned on particular days. The head horseman, Ben Wallage, did most of the carting to and from Stowmarket, Needham Market and, occasionally, Ipswich. Guano (seabird manure from South America) was spread by hand where special treatment was required. Once drilling started, Boy Elijah was scaring rooks full time, but in 1867 he ceased to be Boy Elijah and became Elijah Wallage, though his age is not noted.

J. Hughes was stockman (a family tradition that persisted in the village until recently) and also lambed the flock in spring, assisted by Boy Battle. The threshing engine needed a team of nine men and was probably pulled by a team of horses. Wages were paid fortnightly: the men got 11 shillings a week and boys four shillings. A shilling is five pence today.

By 1872 there was a Donald Larnach at the manor, son of a wealthy London family, who is credited by tradition with keeping up a fashionable state in the village. It is known from Herbert Knock's account books that he sold Mr Larnach considerable amounts of bran for his carriage and riding horses. Larnach was involved with the School Board, which purchased land and built the school in 1874 on the Straight Road. This is now the community centre.

Larnach resigned from the School Board in 1880 and must have moved from the Manor House soon afterwards, for in 1885 the directory shows that Joseph Sturgeon was living at the Manor House as a tenant of the Larnach family, who owned the farm until the end of World War One.

A glimpse of Mr Sturgeon's character can be gained from a story passed down about his worrying nature. Apparently, one of his workmen, who was subject to epileptic fits, was sent to work at St John's Grove, about three-quarters of a mile away from the farm. That night Joseph remembered that he had not seen the man return and, being afraid that he had collapsed, he took a hurricane lantern and searched the fields and woods without success. In the morning it was found that the man had gone home another way and was safely in bed all the time.

Joseph Sturgeon retired from farming to live at Elmswell. His nephew kept up the link with the Knocks, by occasional summer visits to relive his childhood memories of holidays with his uncle at the manor.

The Knock family: chronicling a millenium of residence

Finally, we come to the heroes of our journey through the history of St John's Manor. The Knock family connection started in 1901 when

Herbert John Knock took over the tenancy from Joseph Sturgeon and moved from Rose Farm with his wife, Kate, and two sons, John and Herbert. Both boys started working on the farm when they left school and were paid the princely sum of six shillings a week, which rose to 13s by 1914.

Herbert Knock at this time was approaching 50 years of age and, as well as farming two small farms, Rose Farm and Vale Farm, he had established a thriving business in pork butchery and carrying provisions and animal feed from Needham and Stowmarket for his neighbours. Some of the sidelines had to be run down when he took over the 260 acres of Manor Farm.

Herbert is described as 'a short, thickset man with a long trunk and short legs and a reputation for humour.' He was a strict Plymouth Brethren and worshipped at the Moats Tye Meeting Room at Combs. On occasions he would take his sons quite long distances in a pony and trap to hear a renowned visiting preachers. He was fond of shooting and took his 12-bore gun with him when he visited his men at work around the farm. He and his wife used the kitchen (north) end of the house. He kept special lots of seed corn and other farm stores in the unfurnished drawing room.

Both sons were married when Herbert died in 1916. John Herbert and Edith (née Durrant) were living at Manor Cottages. Herbert Edward, who had married Edith's sister Janet, had moved to Ebbs Farm in Combs. The continual use of the three Christian names of Herbert, John and Edward was to cause much confusion, particularly for the family's bank.

When John had the chance to buy the farm from the Larnach family he moved with his wife and daughter, Mary, into the Manor House. His widowed mother moved to a house in Combs. By this time both brothers had developed an interest in breeding and showing pedigree Shirehorses. Herbert had taken on a much larger farm at Mendlesham and John took on a tenancy on Tollemache Hall at Offton, which he farmed off-hand until 1931. Three more children were born at the manor in the 1920s. However, tragedy struck in 1931 when John's wife, Edith, contracted double pneumonia and died after a long illness.

Manor Farm was typical of the area. The arable land was cropped with beans, peas and clover, followed by barley and oats and then back to beans. A small acreage of roots included sugar beet and a bastard fallow followed one of the ryegrass and trefoil mixtures cut for hay (a bastard fallow left the ground uncropped for only half a year). Little fertiliser was used and fertility was maintained with farmyard manure and a folded flock of store lambs in the summer. Store cattle were brought in (usually north country Shorthorns), grazed on the pastures all summer and fattened in yards in winter. The yard diet was cut chaff with mangolds, oat and bean meal and if available, linseed cake.

The small breeding herd of Large Black or Essex sows were mated with a Large White boar to produce blue and white pigs, which were finished for bacon, often going by rail to Birmingham. The six working horses were usually supplemented by up to four colts of various ages and stages of being broken in to work. All the livestock had to walk to the farm pond twice a day to drink. Water for the pigs was carried in pails and mixed with meal in cut-down casks and fed in cast iron circular troughs.

The six men of the farm were skilled at their jobs, long-serving and good-natured with each other. Apparently they were envied by other workers in the area because they were kept in full employment through the years of depression, when other workers were paid off or went on short-time working.

One of the families that worked on the farm in 1818 was still represented in 1922 – four generations of the Horrex family were connected with the farm. During the hard times of the late 1920s and early 1930s, a significant contribution to the farm income came in the form of eggs from a laying flock. Also, butter was made from the milk of three or four house cows.

The house was part of the poultry enterprise. A 150-egg incubator stood in the corner of the unfurnished drawing room and the chicks, when hatched, were moved upstairs to an empty bedroom. In the autumn this room became the apple store, with space for walnuts (a great favourite with the family) to be laid on sacking to dry. The grounds inside the moat were home to the young pullets, who moved on to the meadow at point-of-lay.

At this time there was a wooden bridge across the moat to gain access to the older poultry. John's wife, Edith, had two great interests. One was rearing poultry of all kinds, including turkeys, geese and ducks as well as chickens. Roses were her other abiding passion, and they were pruned each year by a gardener from Battisford Hall. The climbing roses on the west wall of the house and over arches along a path, as well as roses in beds, provided a blaze of colour in summer.

After Edith's death, John employed a housekeeper to run the house and bring up the children, who at that time went to the village school. John and Joan later went to Stowmarket Secondary School. Herbert, who was probably most affected by the loss of his mother, declined in health and died in 1944.

The war years brought many changes. Due to the construction of RAF Wattisham, a remotely controlled radio beacon was installed just beyond the farm, and as a result mains electricity and the telephone were available in the house. The proximity of the airfield attracted enemy air raids, so the house had one or two near misses from high explosive bombs. Some incendiaries fell among the farm buildings but did little damage.

After the war the pattern of farming changed. Some horses were sold and a tractor was purchased to be driven by the head horseman. Later, in the 1950s, came a combine harvester and trailers to replace the old farm wagons.

In 1938, John Herbert married Elizabeth Aggas. He died in 1969 and Lizzie remained in the house with her niece, who had been living with them for many years. After her death in 1983, it was decided that John and Pat should move to the manor and occupy the southern end of the house, leaving Edith Aggas in the part she had lived in with her aunt. At this time John Edward was approaching retirement from his farm manager's job at Battisford Hall. Work began on the alterations in 1984 and was sufficiently advanced by 1986 for John and Pat to move in. A few years before, John's younger sister, Joan, retired to live at Manor Cottages, where her elder sister, Mary, had been born. Mary married Bill Human and lived at Cambridge.

The alterations to the Manor Farm house were extensive, the most dramatic being the removal of the fireplace in the dining room to reveal an inglenook fireplace with the remains of a smoke jack in the chimney. John used parts of redundant farm machinery to provide extra adornments, including two ornamental candle holders made from harrows, and then placed them either side of the head-carving of St John the Baptist in the wall above the fireplace. The false ceiling in this room was removed to reveal oak beams.

John and Pat, who in September 2003 celebrated their golden wedding anniversary and John's 80th birthday, refer to their own family to bring the story up-to-date. Their eldest son, Edward, was born in 1955. Christopher came next in 1957, and twins Sarah and Penelope were born in 1968. Edward took a degree in applied chemistry and worked first for

John and Pat Knock in the front doorway of St John's Manor.

British Steel and then for Tungstone Batteries at Market Harborough. Christopher read agriculture at Wye College, where many years later his sister Penny read rural environmental studies. Chris describes further education at Writtle College, near Chelmsford, Essex, in a later section.

Penny went on to work for the Forestry Commission as an environmental ranger. During this time she was awarded a Junior Nuffield Scholarship and visited New Zealand and the United States.

A septarian nodule, found in the cellar of the manor house, that is a relic of the Ice Age, left over in the ground when the ice retreated. It is yet another example of the wealth of historic detail to be found in and around St John's Manor.

Sarah received a degree in geography at Durham University and taught for a while before marrying Paul Hill and bringing up a family. Christopher married Margaret Anderson in 1985 and they went to live in part of her father's house in Stowupland with their two children, Georgina and James.

The Knocks have always been an active family in the community, and one of John and Pat's children suggested that they should record some of their activities outside the home. John was a parish councillor for nearly 50 years, and during that time had two spells as chairman. Also, he was twice chairman of the Stowmarket branch of the National Farmers' Union. While John concentrated on parish and union matters, Pat served on the Battisford Parochial Church Council and was a lay reader of the benefice. For a while she was lay chairman of the Bosmere Deanery Synod. With others Pat started the Battisford Elder Club, and she was a school manager and then governor for 20 years.

John and Pat say in conclusion: 'We are aware that there are still gaps in our records which should be filled, and that surprise discoveries may lurk in the house and garden. However, we are determined that St John's Manor will remain our pleasant if unpretentious family home.'

Modern times: alternative enterprises can point the way ahead for the 'average' size Suffolk farm

Representing the modern farming outlook in agriculture's ever-changing scenario is Pat and John Knock's son, Chris, the current Suffolk County

'Strong evidence to suggest that moat, earliest buildings and occupation predate preceptory'

An excavation on the site of the preceptory of the Knights Hospitallers at St John's Manor was a project of the Suffolk Archaeological Field Group in 1988. The intention was to investigate further the walls found in a series of holes dug on the south side of the house by another group the previous year. The expectation was that light would be thrown on the early history of the site, and in particular the relationship between the preceptory and the present building.

The conclusions in the report of the team, headed by Mr R. Carr, say that documentary sources show that there was a preceptory on the site at least as early as the reign of Henry II during the late 12th century. 'Within the rather broad tolerances of our knowledge of the dating of pottery we may suppose that the earliest structure with its date in the 13th century was, therefore, an early part of the preceptory – but not perhaps the very earliest phase,' he comments.

The official dig in 1988.

'The presence of early mediaeval wares and Thetford type wares of the 11th-12th century suggest quite strongly that the moat and the (as yet unlocated) earliest buildings and occupation may predate the foundation of the preceptory.

'There is clear evidence that building work on the preceptory site was of more than one phase, and that at least some of the buildings were destroyed in the 16th or early 17th century and replaced by the present house; within the dating tolerances of pottery this is again an acceptable fit with the dissolution of the Order and the granting of the property to Mr Judde in 1543. It remains possible that the cellars date back to the preceptory but more work is required both on the buildings, the documents and the excavation to confirm this.'

Chairman of the National Farmers' Union. But we have to go back a few years to understand how his thinking, and that of many farmers struggling to cope in the 21st century, has evolved.

When I met Chris at Battisford's Manor Farm in 1996, he was the inventor and successful owner of Hoggies, a pig spit-roasting enterprise run from home. He saw his first pig roasting while working on a pig farm in Germany, the method having similarities to the one-time great British tradition of ox-roasting. He had to go into the forest and help with the cooking of one of the pigs from his unit. 'The way they did it seemed extremely hard work, the chefs taking it in turns to rotate the pig by hand over charcoal for about 10 hours,' he said.

In 1987, after he had been home for a couple of years, the Sudbury Rowing Club asked Chris to do a barbecue for 100 people. 'Stupidly, I said "I'll roast you a pig", then I went home and realised that I would have to make a spit and that it would not be as easy as saying it,' he said. However, he made the spit in the farm workshop – and it worked well. 'Everyone said how fantastic the barbecue was and many asked if I could come back the next year.' Chris's parents attended the club's roast the following year and they told him it would be just the thing for a church summer barbecue. The unique enterprise grew from there, as Chris developed the special skills and confidence to serve the succulent pork and crisp crackling at shows and private parties. He recalls that his best trade always came from downwind customers!

Tyrell's imprisonment in the Tower

The Statute of Dissolution (1540) laid down that on arrival in England, Hospitallers were to present themselves before two senior royal officials and take an Oath of Allegiance to the Protestant King Henry VIII.

By 1541 William Tyrell was confined to the Tower under suspicion of treason. He was not pardoned until March 1543. (The treason referred to was probably treasonable talk overseas). The line between favour and the execution block was a thin one in Tudor England, but Henry could find use for Tyrell's naval talent, as he had captained the galleon of the Order of St John in the late 1530s.

In 1545 tribute was paid to William Tyrell, who was recommended to command the galley wing of the fleet. Tyrell's last commission was appointment as Vice-Admiral in 1556, little over a year before his death.

Youth group in initial dig to trace manor's history

A team of young people from the Bosmere Deanery Youth Group spent a weekend on the first archaeological dig at St John's Manor House. The *East Anglian Daily Times* reported at the time that the group had been trying to discover the whereabouts of a possible hidden cellar.

Mr and Mrs Knock said they were keen to return the house to its original state as much as possible. 'We knew the youth group were keen to help out and earlier in the year they helped to uncover a magnificent fireplace,' Mrs Knock told the newspaper. 'This weekend they have been camping in the grounds and excavating what we believe might be an extension to the cellar which has been blocked off.'

One of the leaders of the group of 17 youths, Judy Hailes, said they were treating the dig as a weekend break.

Housewives experienced in cooking for their families for many years would quiz him on how he produced such crisp crackling, and many complimented him on the juiciness of the pork. He told them that the succulence came from cooking at low temperature for a long period, in complete contrast to most people's everyday experience of having to put a meal on the table in 20 minutes.

It took him seven hours to roast a pig, using experience to work out how, by varying the temperatures – starting it very hot to seal the meat and then taking the temperature right down to cook it long and slow – to keep in the juiciness and succulence that made the meat so tasty.

The pigs he used were standard modern hybrids which would normally sell for bacon. On occasions he cooked old-type pigs such as Tamworths and Berkshires, and found that although the meat was perhaps more flavoursome because the pig was older by the time it was killed, the meat conformation was not there. In his opinion, lumps of fat are in the wrong place in the traditional, old-style breeds, whereas the modern hybrid has 'a fantastic quantity of lean'. The fat on a hybrid is just under the skin, and this is used by the chef to keep the animal basted, and therefore it is, in effect, self-basting.

'As a farmer it gave me a fascinating insight into what people want, and how they want to eat,' said Chris, when I revisited Manor Farm in late May 2003. 'The historical side to it is that we have gone down this modern route of eating portions. Everywhere you go you get a portion, and here (in pig-roasting) we had a method of eating which had nothing to do with portions. You have this whole pig and (for the customer) it is feasting. You have as much as you want, just like the old days, and that was the nice part about it. It meant that people can keep coming back for more, so I always took along too large a pig, because I knew some people would do just that.'

Being the first hog-roasting enterprise in the region, Chris built up the business, eventually roasting 150 pigs a year and employing other people to run five mobile roasting units. But by 1996 six other people were copying the idea, and it was starting to get quite competitive. He also wanted more weekends free for the sake of his young family, so he decided that if someone offered him a good price for Hoggies as a going concern, he would sell the business.

Chris sold Hoggies in 1997, just at a time when the growing number of hog-roasters were developing their own niche market. Some 20 people are now fully employed roasting pigs for special events, and there is stiff competition for the big jobs, he says. The Hoggies business is still run very effectively by a man who works mainly around Cambridge, because, says Chris, that's where there is the most money in the region and that's where he does most of his business. He is pleased that the name of Hoggies is still very well known in the area.

Returning to working on the farm, Chris decided to concentrate on the contract finishing of pigs that he was doing for a local farmer. He had two small sheds – one was finished in 1990, the other in 1998 – and those two sheds housed 700 pigs, Chris taking them from the farmer and rearing them on. However, in the year 2000, when pig prices got very low, the farmer had to close part of his business down, and Chris now contract finishes pigs for a Norfolk firm. Two years ago he built a third, larger shed which takes 1,100 pigs, so that the farm now has room for 1,800 pigs. This has provided the mainstay of farm income for the last two or three years.

On the arable side, ponds and ditches have been cleaned out and also a lot of work has been completed under a Countryside Stewardship scheme. Chris and his father used one of the first CS agreements to revitalise all the hedges, coppicing where they were too large, and filling in gaps. When this finished four years ago, they went straight into a second stewardship scheme, taking some of the arable land out of production and replacing it with grass.

On the other historical sites on the farm, away from the manor house, archaeologists carrying out field-walking found evidence of Saxon houses near some ponds, and Chris grassed-down the area so that, archaeologically, they did not disturb it. 'You don't actually find houses, you find the midden [waste heap],' said Chris. But he is happy enough to find something that predates the Manor House, and only 200 metres away from it.

The other side of the stewardship scheme concerns putting in grass margins next to the hedges, and not farming right up to the hedge gives wildlife a chance to move out from the hedgerow. The family are keen members of the Suffolk Farming and Wildlife Advisory Group, mother Pat until recently having served on the FWAG council for 10 years. Chris is a current council member.

Chris's Monday to Friday job is no longer on the farm. He is the Project Director of an organisation known as ADER, Agricultural Development in the Eastern Region. Funded by the East of England Development Agency, the project helps farmers retrain and develop their businesses away from just relying on growing crops and rearing animals. The scheme, which has been going for only three years, is a partnership between the agricultural colleges, training groups, DEFRA, EEDA (East of England Development Agency), county councils and others – a total of 34 partners make up the organisation. In the short time since it was set up, ADER has worked with more than 3,000 farmers.

ADER's publicity leaflet declares that it is 'a non-profit-making organisation aimed at helping farmers and others involved in the rural economy develop their businesses by providing a co-ordinated range of high quality business support'. The leaflet also says: 'The project aims to give you a sound insight into the management and practical issues that you need to consider when assessing the opportunities on your farm or holding.'

When Chris set up ADER four years ago, everything was looking good at Manor Farm, for at that time the pigs were doing well economically, and so was the arable side. He thought he could maintain farm income with half coming from the pigs and half from arable cropping. But in the past two or three years, the money has gone out of the arable side. Rather than take less money from farming enterprises, Chris thought it better to take another job outside the family farm.

With time on his hands after giving up hog-roasting, he did a degree course at Writtle Agricultural College, near Chelmsford, and from the knowledge he acquired there, and the contacts he made, he became qualified to do the training job. Chris said the enjoyment of the work with

ADER was in knowing that there are lots of farmers that could be helped, just by taking things stage by stage and bringing in the farmer's own ideas. The help and advice they were able to give, building on the farmer's own ideas, has been well received. 'It's not change that is the problem because British farmers, Suffolk farmers in particular, are good at change; it is just the speed of change being asked of them. We are there, if they are feeling left behind, to help them catch up,' he said.

For Chris, it means working on the home farm on Saturday mornings. Two recently dug reservoirs are for the irrigation of sugar beet, and as soon as the work was done, they were spotted by local anglers who 'claimed' them for fishing. Chris said he didn't mean to provide a local amenity, but he now thinks it's great and says the anglers look after the reservoirs very well.

Chris maintains traditional cropping of oilseed rape, winter wheat, sugar beet and spring malting barley – a normal mid-Suffolk rotation. In terms of staff, the farm has gone from having three people working alongside Chris in the mid-1980s, to Chris working full-time by himself and now, today, working on the farm at weekends, while Jonathan Bradley helps part-time with the pigs on weekdays.

Two hundred acres is considered the average size Suffolk farm in the first decade of the 21st century, but Chris admits it is very difficult to make a living from 200 acres. He says that if he has the chance to develop businesses on the farm, moving away from crops and animals, he could return to full-time working, though should the price of pigs and arable cropping come back to profitability, then it might be possible to make more money from what has always been achieved on the farm.

At the moment, however, the whole emphasis on many farms like his own is to look for another source of income, so he is helping farmers who want to set up another, perhaps totally different, enterprise. He sees this as a logical thing to do, but he knows there are quite a few farmers like himself who have ventured off the farm in order to earn an alternative income. This is an increasing trend which, he says, is occupying a lot of people's time and effort.

'It is interesting to look back 30 years, when we all had lots of enterprises on the farms,' said Chris. 'When my father was farming, and I was a boy, there would be some beef cattle, some pigs and before that, some sheep, and there would be lots of different arable crops.' All the way through the seventies and eighties, farmers became more and more specialised. Nowadays, however, it it is being realised that it was the

breadth of the variety of enterprises in the past which gave security of
income. 'I think we are going back to where we were 20 or 30 years ago
as far as the number of enterprises goes,' said Chris. 'There will be lots of
farms in the future where they will rent out a couple of buildings, so that
they will have rental income, and perhaps have a separate business in
another building. They might also have an old building which becomes a
residential property – all these things farmers can start to do, but haven't
needed to do previously. It a sign of the times.'

He sees the farmhouse as a good place to live, with owners looking for
alternative uses for buildings, and that would see money coming into
farming as farmers are increasingly seen as custodians of the countryside.
That scenario was now taking shape and there was a growing realisation
that that is what is happening.

'I am reasonably excited about the future,' he said. 'I think there is a
lot of potential there actually to base quite a few businesses out in the
countryside. If we want to revitalise village communities, let's put some
small businesses within those communities, so that there are people
moving about in the daytime. One of the things you spot is that villages
which don't have any means of employment do become dormitories, their
residents moving out in the morning and coming back in the evening.
Those villages which have places of employment seem to be far more vital
because they keep their local services going.'

CHAPTER 2

Priory Farm, Preston St Mary

If a farmer fills his barn with grain, he gets mice. If he leaves it empty,
he gets actors.
– Bill Vaughan, American author (1915–1977)

Adrian and Jane Thorpe were the genial hosts at their home, Priory Farm, Preston St Mary, near Lavenham, for a Historical Farm Walk arranged by the Suffolk Farming and Wildlife Advisory Group, in conjunction with the Suffolk Institute of History and Archaeology, on a glorious shirt-sleeve evening in June 2003. I joined a large party from the two organisations, split up into five groups to walk the farm and listen to five speakers in turn. The speakers were: Tom Williamson, a lecturer in Landscape History, who explained some features of the historic landscape including its ancient woodland and more recent hedges; Philip Aitkens, historic buildings consultant, who described the mediaeval features of the house and farm buildings; Vic Scott, an excavation finds supervisor, who interpreted the site of an excavation dig taking place on the farm; Rob Parker, a butterfly conservationist, who discussed a plantation designed to encourage rare butterflies; and Adrian Thorpe, the host, who outlined his farming operations and illustrated how it is possible to combine farming with conservation.

The front of the farmhouse at Priory Farm, on the historical farm open day.

A 300-acre farm which balances cropping with flora and fauna

Adrian Thorpe, owner of the moated Priory Farm with wife Jane, explained his farming policy for the 300-acre farm growing winter wheat, winter barley and spring break crops in equal acreage proportions. 'We

The changing Priory Farm. These two maps show how the field patterns and names have changed in the area of Priory Farm between 1839, when the tithe map on the left was drawn, and the present day.

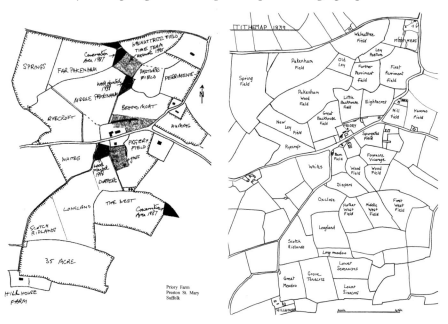

like our spring-sown crops because we can leave the land unploughed, just leave it as stubble until November,' he said. Break crops this year are peas for seed, soya beans, cress for seed (grown for Church of Bures and seen for the first time on the farm), and also a little bit of linseed.

The Thorpes had been into Countryside Stewardship for quite a long time, having two-metre grassy flower margins around most of the fields. There are also some six-metre margins. The *Time Team* site, which is also now under stewardship, is down to grass to protect the archaeology from being damaged by ploughing, and Adrian gets a payment for this.

In 2003 they joined the new arable options. Stewardship was trying to fine-tune the scheme with the money they pay specifically to save key endangered species, and farmers must name the species they are trying to help, in this case the turtle dove. This is achieved at Priory Farm by sowing three small areas of bird seed mixture which are renewed every few years.

Moving on to the recent renovation of a smaller ancient barn, on grassland away from the other farm buildings and which, he said, had not been repaired in living memory, Adrian said the barn's construction was a wonderful example of timbers being reused, and he was quite pleased with the result of the renovation because it now fitted into the landscape. Wattle and daub is prominent in its construction.

Adrian and Jane have been lent some Norfolk Horn sheep, which were an endangered breed with only three ewes and a ram at one time, but the breed had been crossed with another breed to give them a broader genetic base, and now there were plenty of them. Adrian thinks they are lovely sheep. Adrian pointed out the line of the moat, a now rare black poplar tree and the site where a cottage once stood. The area to him was 'a bit of old England', as he also remembered there was once a Victorian windmill where sheep now graze, but which was gone by 1900.

A barn that beams with pride and echoes of a television rogue

A billboard prop on my second visit to Priory Farm in the mid-1990s announced 'Cavendish Auctions. Sale of Fine Furniture.' It was at that time the only obvious remaining sign in the barn that *Lovejoy* had been there. As it happened, 'Lovejoy Country' did not prove to be as enduring as the region's Constable Country, but it remains in the memory for many enthusiasts of BBC Television's alternative and entirely fictional *Antiques Roadshow* set in East Anglia.

The 'Cavendish Auctions' sign of the BBC Television Lovejoy *series.*

The ghosts of the likeable rogue and his merry band somehow still linger among the exposed beams and rafters of the beautiful old barn that was the saleroom setting for many a dubious deal. I remember Adrian and Jane Thorpe recalling with some satisfaction how the stars of the show and support crew would arrive at regular intervals for several days of filming over a period of almost two years. Their famous visitors were, in return, just as fascinated to see a filled grain store and other aspects of the farm's harvest operations.

'They had no idea how hard farmers worked,' said Jane. 'I think they thought it was all rather cushy, and they were absolutely amazed'. The whole entourage would suddenly arrive without warning to park their equipment in store three or four days before filming. One day, during harvest, they arrived when Adrian was down the field with his trailer. When he returned to the house, he found the TV crew had parked their ancient Bedford dining bus right across the entrance to where his combine was under cover. They had locked up the bus and had gone.

Next day the question was how to move the dining bus to get the combine out. They knew where the key was because farm worker Derick Howe had seen where they left it, but still no one could start the ancient Bedford diesel which was at least 20 or 30 years old. They had almost given up when it was figured out that there was a special way of heating the fuel.

The *Lovejoy* series proved to be Adrian and Jane's favourite diversification throughout its duration. Income covered what they had spent on the barn, enabling them to spruce up the cloakrooms to a high standard for future use. Following the departure of the television paraphernalia, the ancient barn was turned into a function hall and licensed for marriage ceremonies. These take place there on most weekends during the summer.

How Suffolk farmers benefited from the Napoleonic wars

Historic buildings consultant Philip Aitkens referred to the buildings at Priory Farm as a complete homestead, saying that the house was the oldest building on the site, dating from the second half of the 15th century, most likely from between 1450 and 1470. Another group of farmstead buildings were all built at a later date, but they contain components from older buildings. Philip believes that these buildings may date from the time of the Napoleonic wars. 'Whenever there is a war, farms benefit,' he said, 'because trade routes are damaged and home-grown produce is expensive, so farmers make good profits.' During the first quarter of the 19th century many Suffolk farms were redeveloped as a result, and on the gable end of the house at Priory Farm was a brick with the date 1807. There was another dated brick on the garden wall, believed to be from 1812. The two dates, he thought, would resonate with anyone interested in that period.

The speaker also believed that, like so many Suffolk farms, the site was flattened, perhaps not in the same year but in the same sort of period, leaving just the house standing during a historically traumatic period. 'No

Historic buildings consultant Philip Aitkens.

doubt they also ploughed up pastures, flattened hedges, and so forth, to
grow more corn, and the result often was that barns were enlarged, other
buildings were converted, new buildings were added, all for the purpose
of producing more grain at high speed.'

The yard in the centre would be awash with animals, mostly cattle, but
during the Napoleonic period cattle were not very popular, and herds
were being reduced in size. In fact, many farms in this area were getting
rid of almost all their animals. It was very much wheat-growing country,
with heavy clay soil. Piles of wheat would have been brought into the
barn, deposited to left and right on the threshing floor and later brought
down to be threshed at a more convenient moment. The corn would then
be taken away to the granary.

As nothing was wasted, the chaff would be fed to the horses, and there
would have been other uses for the straw. Priory Farm barn was in two
parts, having a second floor at right angles and giving the effect of a two-
floor barn, so by about 1812 they had, in effect, two floored barns for the
corn. Because the barn was full of previously used timbers, it was his
contention that they had been taken from farm buildings that had been
demolished for that purpose. He did not think there was anything major
in the construction that predated the Napoleonic period.

The aisle in the building gave more space for storing sheaves of corn
than otherwise would have been possible. The aisle tradition, he said,
went back into the Middle Ages, and the earliest examples he knew of
were from the 12th and 13th century. 'This is certainly by no means that
age, this is very much a circa 1800 structure; many of the timbers are cut
specially for the purpose'. He also said that there were other indicators to

*Inside the beautiful
aisled barn at Priory
Farm.*

suggest that it was a Napoleonic wars period structure, pointing out bits from a previous building, some heavily weathered or showing wear where animals had rubbed on the walls and timber of earlier buildings.

Some of these timbers may have come not from a barn, but from, say, a stable or even from a house, although there is no evidence for this so it seems likely that they came from previous farm buildings on the site. He was suggesting, in principle, that previously there had been a good 16th century barn on the site, possibly with stabling as well, which was taken down in about 1800. The bits from the structure(s) had probably been put in a pile and the carpenter had chosen what he wanted, selecting principal timbers for principal situations in the 'new' building. Other pieces were reduced in size to be used for studs and rafters, with new timber being cut where necessary as well.

Summarising his own thoughts on ancient barns, Philip Aitkens prefaced his remarks by saying that someone who specialised in barns in Essex had once said to him: 'I see barns as graveyards.' 'I think that's a lovely phrase for it. If the timbers are no longer suitable for reconstructing the house that they have just demolished, the timbers are good enough for the barn. Even with their weather-wearing, they still have enough guts to keep going for a couple of generations in a rebuilt barn, so they use the timbers there. For people like myself, it is a goldmine. It tells us about previous generations of buildings on the site, even though those buildings are long gone. So barns of this period, even the late Georgian period, can give us a great deal of information about the long history of the site back into the Middle Ages, so we mustn't despise them. We cannot list them, they are not usually protected, but we ought to analyse them before it is too late.'

With specific reference to Priory Farm barn, Aitkens had noticed that there was a stable in one corner which was not very exciting to him because it had been pulled about. However, it came from the 19th century and was an important part of the evolution of the site. It had one piece of wood in it which he did find very exciting. The wood was now used as a purlin, a supporting member in the plane of the roof. It was in two sections, made of oak, and it had been carved. At intervals there were square carvings, with Tudor flowers, the kind of quality of carving found in church roofs or, very occasionally, roofs of high quality in houses dating from the end of the 15th century. The piece of wood in question may have come from a church not very far from the farm or, conceivably, from a demolished house of high status. But it was more likely to have come from a church. 'What church was being altered here around 1812 or thereabouts, such that they could afford to throw away a beautifully carved piece of timber?' he pondered.

The speaker said there were also open shelter buildings in the yard. These were for a herd of cattle, perhaps being fattened in the yard. The straw would be piled up for bedding and progressively mucked on by the cattle, and it was then used as fertiliser when the cattle were taken away for slaughter as beef. That was in the early 19th century.

Philip Aitkens asked his audience to imagine the farmstead teeming with animals. 'It would be mucky, nothing like today,' he said. Animals were very important to the economy of the period, so it was necessary for visitors to decide where the grain zone was, where the zone was for rearing animals and also how the two were inter-related. 'If you were going onto a wealthy site like this in the 19th century, the whole group would be integrated and designed in such a way as to minimise labour and to maximise efficiency and output,' he said. 'That kind of farming was being introduced in the 19th century, but it didn't work out in Suffolk, because of poverty. Suffolk was going through so much difficulty that the farmers were still hiring their labourers incredibly cheaply. These poor old boys were still threshing away by hand, when in other parts of England they had machinery to do it. So Suffolk at that period, in the mid-19th century, was way behind, poverty-stricken and still doing things in the traditional way.'

He said that on the Hengrave Hall Estate, there had been a riot in the 1840s over poor wages, and the labourers had burnt down the barn on the estate. A new barn was built and dated with a plaque on the front to explain why it had been built. The new barn had a new horse gin, an arrangement for corn grinding, attached to the front. 'That's where the plaque was attached to say the old barn had been destroyed – and here's a new one. The farmer was jolly well going to go ahead no matter how much the men rioted.'

As the group entered the ground floor of the house, Philip Aitkens told us that the main fireplace in the living room was inserted in the early 16th century, to replace an open hearth burning on the floor. At a third period, probably around 1600, the floor was inserted above the hall, closing off a chamber upstairs and losing completely the smoke-blackened roof. In the layout of the open hall, at one end there were two service rooms above the cross-passage and at the other end was a parlour, a sleeping room with a chamber above it.

The fireplace in the ground floor living room.

The cross-passage was a mediaeval tradition that went right through to the 17th century, but by the time the chimney stack had been built, it became much less of a passage and more just a part of the room. Occupants went through just behind the chimney stack, around it and into the living room. The single-flue stack had a wide fireplace, but this had since been reduced. However, the interior of the fireplace has its original brickwork with an arch-headed seat. The original finish of the brickwork was pink, and the term ruddle, he said, was the right one. There were clear traces of the ruddle on the arch dating from the original construction of the chimney, and Philip asked us to imagine the whole chimney stack soaring up into the roof complete with the ruddling on it, and quite likely white lines painted over that. The lintel, which once spanned the fireplace opening, was also in evidence.

The few remaining aisled barns are 'immensely precious'

In his article on aisled barns for *An Historical Atlas of Suffolk*, historic buildings consultant Philip Aitkens refers to the need in an English climate for farmers to put their annual harvest results under cover with haste. He says that for 700 years at least, this need was met in Suffolk by the largest and most valuable of all farm buildings – a timber-framed barn.

By extending the roof slopes down to about 2 to 2.5 metres from the ground, extra space could be made behind the main posts along each side.

At first these aisled barns only appeared on manorial and monastic sites, where resources enabled them to be built on a massive scale.

However, it is estimated that although 15 mediaeval aisled barns remain in Suffolk, only three have original roofs, and most have undergone other major alterations. The few complete survivors are therefore immensely precious, he says. Other barns were completely rebuilt at a later date, but from the same components. For example, Philip Aitkens discovered that a vanished mediaeval barn shown on a map of 1594 at Lower Farm, Risby, was rebuilt in the 17th century 30 metres from the original site: it incorporates parts of the old barn and the old farmhouse. A 17th-century barn at Whepstead Hall (since converted to houses) has 12 main posts, five tiebeams and many other timbers taken from the manorial barn of c.1300 which must have stood on the same site.

Philip Aitkens says that all Suffolk barns have certain features in common. Smaller barns were entered at the centre of one side by a pair of divided doors, high enough to take wagons loaded with sheaves. The sheaves were thrown to one side, and later brought back onto the paved floor inside the doors for threshing. Larger barns of six or more bays had two doorways, and smaller doors were normally provided opposite in the rear wall. Half of the later barns have only one aisle, at the rear: the extra space won by this aisle was at the expense of a row of obtrusive posts and braces, which was considered worthwhile – even after 1800 in a few cases.

Archaeological dig on one of several mediaeval sites

Visitors to Priory Farm joined excavation finds supervisor Vic Scott at the site of a mediaeval dig. He told us there are at least six other mediaeval sites on the farm, plus sites from other periods, with the possible exception of Anglo-Saxon. Opposite the present site is an old road which, as far as is known, used to lead to Lavenham, and it was along this road that most of the other mediaeval sites are situated It was thought to be a peasant farmer's site, but no building had been found.

Prior to 1992 the area of the dig was arable land, and when it was being cultivated there were lots of early bits of pottery being brought up from the clay soil. A selection of these was shown to members of the Suffolk Archaeological Unit, who were mildly interested and suggested putting in a trial trench to see if the source of the pottery could be found. So Adrian Thorpe, a member of the Suffolk Institute Field Group, and

Archaeological dig
supervisor Vic Scott.

An archaeological dig being carried out at Priory Farm.

other interested people, began a trial trench 10 years ago. They discovered that the trench cut through a ditch which was full of 14th-century pottery.

The diggers reached a point where they required professional guidance. 'Fortunately, a member of the Suffolk Archaeological Unit lived only a couple of villages away, and the field group have occasionally called on him when anything interesting has been found. The dig has continued on a weekly basis over the past 10 years, normally on a Monday, weather permitting, and usually from about Easter to October. One snag is that the land has a high water table, so after heavy rain a trench will fill with water.'

The work is carried out by a nucleus of some six field group members and two were present specially for the historical farm walk. The excavations to date have been in ditches and pits, and they have found plenty of shards from the 13th and 14th century – hundredweights of them over 10 years, all still on the farm and the best of them on display in the barn. Pottery was reconstructed where it was possible to do so, and the group also found slag from metal working, oyster shells and shells from large burrowing snails in quite large numbers in certain areas of the ditches.

In the absence of buildings being found, it was felt that the area of the finds was more likely to be the midden of the farmstead, in the working area of the farm, not the building area. Most of the pots appeared to have been made by the same local potter, and some of them are a bit crude. One pot that the speaker said had been put together a few days earlier had a hole in the base where the soot had come through, and it was possible that the hole had appeared because the pot had been allowed to boil dry, so the user had thrown it away.

There had been very few metal finds over the years. Early on in excavations they had found a bronze brooch, about the size of a new

Pottery unearthed at Priory Farm, dating from the 12th to the 14th century.

A large showy jug of the Rouen type. Hedingham ware.

Roman pottery found during earlier excavations.

penny, and a ring of twisted bronze with a tongue on it like a buckle. The archaeological unit dated that to between 1200 and 1350. More recently they had found a 14th-century iron hunting arrow head.

The best find, however, had come from the bottom of the pit, about 4ft 6in down – a solid bronze leg from a Roman statuette. It was of very high quality with a lot of detail on it. It had been estimated from the size of the leg that the complete statuette would have been about 18 inches tall. It was sent to an expert at Oxford who identified it as of British manufacture, depicting a Roman god and of exceptional quality. It would have come from either a villa site or a temple site, though neither had been found on the farm.

The statuette fragment was found about 500 metres from where some years ago television's *Time Team* had excavated a Roman site and found footings of only timber and clay, nothing of high quality, just an industrial area. 'So we don't know what it (the statuette leg) was doing at the bottom of a 14th-century rubbish pit,' said Mr Scott. A suggestion was that it came from Colchester and was taken to Preston St Mary to be melted down.

The most recent find of any significance was a Scottish silver penny found in 2002, which dated back to 1290. Although not on show on this occasion, over the years there have been some 500 Roman coins found on the farm's four or five Roman sites by detectorists using the archaeological unit's metal detectors. In fact, the *Time Team* site was found by field walking, a lot of which was undertaken before any

> ## It took 200 small oaks to build average mediaeval house in Suffolk
>
> Oliver Rackham, a Fellow of Corpus Christi College, Cambridge, says in *An Historical Atlas of Suffolk* that Suffolk was less wooded than most counties in mediaeval England. The whole county had once been covered by wildwood, but most of this was destroyed in prehistoric times to make farmland or heath. What remained in the Middle Ages was regularly managed and conserved, either as woodland or wood-pasture.
>
> It is unfortunate for modern-day historians that the Domesday Book lists Suffolk woodlands not in terms of their areas, but by the number of pigs that were supposed to fatten on their acorns. This, says Rackham, was not a realistic way of enumerating woodland.
>
> Woodland was scarce and valuable, although it was not the only source of trees, for Suffolk had plenty of hedges, as attested by an expert on hedges, speaking during a historical walk at Priory Farm, Preston St Mary. Woods were protected by great banks and ditches around them.
>
> The average mediaeval Suffolk house contains some 200 small oaks, representing a year's growth of the *timber* component of about 200 acres of woodland. Only the better wooded districts could have been self-sufficient in timber and wood, even in rural areas.

excavations were carried out. The trenches of the *Time Team* site were filled in once the work had been completed.

Hooper's hypothesis on hedges is perhaps sometimes right

Tom Williamson, a landscape historian at the University of East Anglia, talked initially during the Priory Farm walk about 'Hooper's hypothesis', which he said was dreamt up back in the late 1960s by the botanist/ecologist Max Hooper. He studied lots of hedges and came up with his simple equation, translated in laymen's terms: 'If you take a 30-yard length of hedge and count the number of shrub species in it, and multiply that by 100, it will give you the age of the hedge.'

Hooper did make a lot of important observations, but according to our speaker, it is just not possible to date hedges by the number of species, and he gave two of many reasons for that. One was that the seed supply was very variable throughout the country. 'In an area like this where there are lots of old hedges and a fair bit of woodland, there is all sorts of stuff coming in,' he said. 'In the Midlands, for example, maple is an indicator of an old hedge, that's because the Midlands doesn't have much ancient woodland and was largely unhedged in the Middle Ages.'

Another problem, taken more seriously, was that Hooper's hypothesis assumed that hedges were planted with one species. 'That isn't true,' the speaker argued. 'Before the 18th century hedges were often planted with a range of species. In, say, the 14th century, you couldn't get hold of a lot of hawthorn, it was very difficult because there were no commercial nurseries. So you had to plant a hedge with what you could get from the local woods.'

Hedgerow expert Tom Williamson.

Farmers didn't just view a hedge as a stock-proof barrier. In a pre-industrial peasant economy, hedges were seen as a resource. In the 18th century one writer described hedges as the 'collieries of this country' because they were coppiced for firewood. 'The normal way of managing hedges in this part of East Anglia was that you had them coppiced on a long rotation,' said Williamson. 'You would get masses of wood out of it. Although there are a lot of woods in Suffolk, and there would be a lot of pollarded trees, hedges would still supply masses of wood.' To some extent, hedges were also used as fodder, and in the Middle Ages they were certainly using elm and oak as fodder.

The speaker invited someone from the group to pace out 30 yards – students, he said, usually exaggerated this John Cleese fashion – and the rest were asked to count the number of species in the section. Seven were counted, so according to Hooper's hypothesis, the hedge should be 700 years old. 'It probably is,' Tom Williamson laughed, 'it is that kind of order of magnitude. It's what you would expect from a latish mediaeval hedge'. However, it was not just a matter of simply counting the species, the basic structure of the hedge was also important in the dating process. The subject hedge has sloe more or less as a constant all the way down, while the other species, among them maple and hazel, are in clumps but not large banks. The preferred species for hedge planting were always hawthorn or sloe, which are both thorny and quick growing.

A Suffolk attempt to reintroduce the Grizzled Skipper butterfly

Leading all the groups in turn to a conservation area at Priory Farm, butterfly conservationist Rob Parker, a member of Butterfly Conservation, told us that he now spent all his time chasing butterflies that were common in his youth. 'The butterfly distribution around the country has suffered, and quite a lot of butterflies have lost the habitat they used to enjoy, either because the ground has been ploughed up, sprayed or covered in concrete,' he said.

The natural diversity has changed quite a lot, but on the conservation patch, as well as trees that were growing, there is quite a good diversity of wildflowers growing among the grass, and that is nectar to the bees. The farm has attracted a lot of bumble bees when the bumble bee population nationwide has done badly over the past 20–30 years. Farm owner Adrian Thorpe had told Rob that one of his neighbours, who keeps bees, had a harvest of honey that was better than ever in 2003.

Adrian had remembered that wild strawberry was the food plant of the Grizzled Skipper, a butterfly which used to be common around the county, but was lost in the 1960s. The last time it was seen in the county was in 1967, in Felsham Hall Wood, some five miles from Preston St Mary. Adrian's idea was to see if it was possible to grow a patch of wild strawberry as a place to re-establish the butterfly. 'Butterfly Conservation has lots of reservations about things like that,' said Rob. 'It is not quite like casting wild seed in the countryside and just letting wild flowers grow, because 95 per cent of attempted reintroductions fail, and they fail because the butterfly has quit for some good reason – the habitat has changed and it is no longer suitable.'

The areas in Britain where Grizzled Skippers are found these days are Wiltshire, Dorset and the South Downs, usually doing well in places where there are chalk downs, a south-facing slope and a warm

Wild strawberries growing in the conservation area.

microclimate – a number of things not found in Suffolk. Wild strawberry, while nice for the butterflies, is not all that they need. They do need more habitat and to be able to fly a kilometre in any direction and find the same habitat on return. 'Nonetheless, we did put a lot of effort into it and we did prepare a case that led to Butterfly Conservation agreeing that we could do a trial reintroduction here, monitored by an ecology student, to see how the butterfly fared for a few years,' he said. 'If the selected butterflies were to lose their lives in the venture, then that would be all that was lost, whereas, if it were to surprise us and flourish, we would all be rather pleased about it. Well, it hasn't happened yet because we haven't managed to get everything together. I'm very conscious that the site is not ideal and that these trees are growing, and in 10 years time there will be so much shade here that the place won't be so suitable anymore.'

As hardly anyone in the group knew what a Grizzled Skipper looked like, Rob passed one around, which, he said, had been 'prepared earlier.' He said it was basically black with white spots and looked a bit like a moth, making it easy to overlook. If people had them on their land, they wouldn't necessarily recognize it, he thought. But it was a butterfly that demanded a lot of nectar and would only fly in places where the wildflowers were good.

Butterfly expert Rob Parker.

The conservation area on the farm is good for all kinds of invertebrates, and Rob thought some of them would do well. He said people tended to think of the basic food plant of the butterfly as being nettle, though that is not really true. Many more butterflies feed on grass than on nettle. There are no less than 10 species in Suffolk that feed on grass, including the July butterflies – Meadow Brown, Ringlet, Gatekeeper, the smaller Essex Skippers and Large Skippers, all of which have survived the winter as tiny caterpillars right down in the grass stems.

Rob said those who cut, roll, fertilise and apply weedkiller on their lawns at the end of the year get no butterflies in their gardens. That was why there were never any butterflies in the Abbey Gardens in Bury St Edmunds. 'So if you want to do one small thing for the benefit of the butterfly population, whether you have a farm or a garden, all you have to do is put the lawnmower in the garden shed, and leave it there, because if butterflies are going to breed anywhere, the place they will choose is where the grass grows to maturity,' Rob commented. Generally, this is down the side of hedgerows, in the matted grass that agriculture doesn't reach, and it is in those places that the invertebrates survive.

*Priory Farm owner
Adrian Thorpe.*

A new era at Priory Farm

In the spring of 2004, Adrian Thorpe told me of he and Jane's plans to retire to Hertfordshire, a major decision for them as Priory Farm had been in the ownership of the family since 1934. The farm had been offered for sale at guide prices of £1.65 million for the farm, barn and house, and £300,000 in respect of a cottage and paddock.

A buyer for the farm had been found and, at the time of writing, an East Anglian farmer was expected to take over custodianship in the autumn and continue farming and also the marriage and reception businesses.

Priory Farm has continued to make the news in 2004, the Thorpes having reached the final of *The Times* newspaper's best back garden competition featured on television, adding a further dimension to the many other awards won by the farm in recent years.

CHAPTER 3

Kentwell Hall, Long Melford

The stately homes of England
How beautiful they stand
Amid their tall ancestral trees
O'er all the pleasant land.
– Felicia (Dorothea) Heman (1793–1835)

Kentwell Hall's authentic view of rural life in the 16th century

Special among the large manorial estates in Suffolk opening their gates and doors to the public is 16th-century Kentwell Hall in the village of Long Melford, near Sudbury, nationally famous for its historical re-creations of the Tudor era, depicted in costume by hundreds of keen followers of that period.

During a few weeks of high summer, these enthusiasts dress authentically in the clothes befitting their high-born or serf status in the social order of the reign of King Henry VIII, and speak a long-forgotten form of the English tongue that is strange and baffling to the ears of the 21st-century onlooker. They present a living tableau of a colourful era.

The spectacular front elevation of Kentwell Hall, Long Melford.

Attending the first of these special events, during June 2003, my wife and I were paying customers with members of my family visiting from the state of Oregon in the 'New World' of North America. Passing through a time tunnel and exchanging new money for the groats and pennies of the past, we stepped back in time exactly four-and-a-half centuries, to the year 1553.

Laid out before us was the self-supporting farm and semi-industrial complex of those with individual skills, all explained in a Time Traveller's Guide leaflet which provides a comprehensive explanation of the hard life (for commoners), but relatively simple life for the aristocrats of Tudor England. Here we saw the animal keepers, woodsmen, cartwrights, basket-makers, alchemists, cloth dyers, potters, washerwomen, brick-makers, waterbailiffs and more – everyone had their place in a life that supported not only themselves but the privileged family in the Great Hall. It was normal for the lord of the manor and his family and friends to consume in one day's feasting, the quantity of food consumed by his army of workers in a week.

Most of the folk not engaged in the wool trade of the times laboured in farming, using primitive methods to produce low yields of a limited

A representation of Elizabeth Clopton, from Kentwell's owning family of the 16th century, singing to a lute.

range of crops and looking after a range of animals often housed within the domestic living quarters. Most workers were paid by the year and had to work the full year to be paid at all. Some were paid by the hour at a rate set by the Justices, but still others were paid by the piece: the usual day rate of sixpence would buy, say, six pullets, and it would take three days work to buy a fine capon.

The farm at Kentwell Hall is traditional in the sense that for centuries, mixed farms in East Anglia raised a whole range of animals as well as growing arable crops. Today the majority of farms in the region are exclusively arable, have milking herds or raise pigs or poultry.

Kentwell's owners say their regime is more of a working farm than just an animal display. They raise pigs, sheep and cattle in the traditional non-intensive way for meat, which is on sale in the shop or to order, and sell pedigree stock which is also exhibited in competitive classes at regional agricultural shows. The sheep's fleeces are also sold privately and through the Wool Marketing Board, and some are spun, woven and dyed on the premises. Goats and a range of fowl are also kept.

The Suffolk horses are also working animals, helping as draught horses about the farm and giving cart rides to visitors. There is also a wide range of early farm implements and equipment which is both used and put on show. The farm has a range of traditional timber-framed buildings; light horse and heavy horse stables; pig sties and farrowing pens; a cow byre, aisled barns, a granary, cart lodges, fowl houses, goat houses and more. These all illustrate the basic layout of a working farm and show the types of animals that might have been seen on a mixed farm in past centuries.

Kentwell Hall is recognised as one of England's finest moated Tudor houses, and was described by *Country Life* as 'The epitome of many people's images of an Elizabethan house.' It was built and enhanced by successive members of the Clopton family in the first half of the 16th century on riches derived from the wool trade (John Clopton also having had the magnificent Long Melford Parish Church built at that time), and the exterior of the building has remained unchanged since. However, the interior shows the changes wrought by successive owners culminating in the 'improvements' made in the 1820s by Thomas Hopper in the Gothic style. The building exhibits some of the very best Tudor brickwork in all its variety, bonds and hues.

Representing Elizabeth Clopton and her cousin, William Clopton.

Kentwell's website emphasises that the hall is not a stately home stuffed with museum pieces, 'it is a lived-in house full of interest and vitality, which exudes a strong sense of history.' After the Clopton family died out, the house had a succession of different private owners. It has been the cherished home of Patrick and Judith Phillips and their family since 1971, and is one of the most remarkable private restoration projects of the age, with work still continuing.

The owners invite visitors to stroll through the house with its working Tudor kitchen and magnificent hall with minstrels' gallery. They have also

Two maids supping pottage.

Wench in bakehouse mixing dough.

Swordsman practising his art with a broadsword.

Service building of c.1500, known as the moat house – believed to be the only one of its type for the period in Britain.

decorated, furnished and equipped the main rooms of the house. Outside is a Tudor rose maze in the courtyard, and the part-timbered moat house is an original service building dating from around 1500, with a dairy, bakehouse and brewhouse to service the estate.

16th century records of farming at Kentwell Hall

Kentwell Hall's owner, Patrick Phillips QC, has in his possession 16th-century records of farming at Kentwell Hall, items of which he related to me on a subsequent visit in January 2004.

On 26 April 1571, for example, it is written that the estate had 276 sheep, of which 60 were wethers, 15 rams, and the rest were ewes with 67 lambs. There were also heifers, bulls and steers, as well as '23 milk beasts and 12 northern heifers.' The farm was also using draught oxen.

An inventory for 1578 lists swine: 18 (great) and 16 (less) hogs, and 18 store pigs. There were 53 'lambs of own breeding bought in Norfolk' – Mr Phillips believes this is one of the earliest references to Norfolk Horn sheep. Today's estate also has a number of animals of the Norfolk breed, many of which are believed to be descendants of the original flock. Other rare breeds kept at Kentwell Hall, not only for the delight of the many

Minstrels providing background music for guests in the house.

thousands of visitors but also for exhibiting at agricultural shows, include Tamworth and Gloucester Old Spot pigs, Longhorn cattle, Suffolk horses, Dorset sheep, goats and lots of fowl of various species and rare breeds. A livestock inventory for September 1579 lists: 'Suffolk sheep 44, Suffolk lambs 27, Norfolk lambs 53.'

Lady chats to a scrivener while working on her embroidery.

Wench with child having mid-day pottage.

Wench taking the shade on a hot summer's day.

Arable produce was stored in the Tudor house. An entry for 6 May 1579 opens in the language of the day: 'A brief note of my master his corn.' This relates to 52 quarters of barley delivered to the maltsters. There is an abundance of evidence in the farm records that much of the grain and other arable produce was stored in various parts of the house, including the minstrels' gallery and the Great Chamber, an upstairs room, until required for sale or home use. There are other references to consignments (weighed in quarters) of white wheat, red wheat and old malt – all stored in the house. Seven quarters of white wheat are shown to have been laid in the Long Gallery, a room at the top of the house.

CHAPTER 4

Wantisden Hall Farm, Wantisden

*I like trees because they seem
more resigned to the way they
have to live than other things do.*
– Willa (Sibert) Cather, 1873–1947

History plays a big part in the philosophy of the Kemball family on the Wantisden Hall Farms Estate, near Orford. The woodland areas of Staverton Park and The Thicks, within the estate, have the largest area of ancient pollarded oaks in Europe, the only comparable place being Windsor Great Park.

Some of the trees standing today are believed to be nearly 700 years old, and the park is therefore of great historical and also of conservation interest. Located in the parish of Wantisden, whose ancient spelling of 'Wantisdena' means wooded valley of want, the name Staverton Park covers three blocks of woodland called The Park, The Thicks and Little Staverton. They total around 280 acres, but the original boundaries of the park extended to at least 370 acres.

The name of Staverton is thought to be of Saxon origin, either from the word 'steofar' meaning slaughter, or from 'place of staves.' It is said that the ancient oaks 'witnessed the fierce strife between Angles and Wends in

The parish of Wantisden, also showing Bentwaters airfield and Staverton Park.

the 10th century, where tumuli were thrown over the fallen heroes.' This is thought to be the 'slaughter' which gave rise to the name of Staverton.

The park was more than likely created as a hunting ground by enclosing open woodland and rough pasture between earthen banks. In 1086, the Domesday Book refers to 'woodland for thirty swine for the Manor of Stavertuna.' However, it has been supposed that the actual date of emparkment of the mature trees was 1178, because the Pipe Rolls of that year record a sharp increase in rent to the king. It was around this time that the inhabitants of the park began to change, with the introduction of rabbits by the Normans, and the last wolf being sighted in 1150.

During the 13th century, records of Staverton Park show that bark was stripped from the felled oaks and sold for tanning leather, acorns were sold for fattening pigs, wood was sold for timber or fuel and grazing rights were let for stock. Later, probably in the 16th century, many of the standing oaks were pollarded at 50-year intervals and hence formed into the present shape of crown oaks when pollarding ceased.

There is an earthwork in the northern end of the park (now in the deer enclosure), which is shaped as a horseshoe and called Cumberland's Mound. This has been linked with the 1381 Peasants' Revolt, in which Staverton Hall in Eyke, owned by the Baron of the Exchequer, was burnt to the ground in the rampage. However, the Kemball family have found it difficult to find any evidence to corroborate this, and it is now thought that the mound was probably a mediaeval deer stockade. It is today listed as an ancient monument.

In 1540 the 'farm of Staverton Park' is recorded in an inventory of particulars for a grant to Thomas, Duke of Norfolk, but in 1549 the park was sold to the priors of Butley Abbey. It was the year before this acquisition that the monks recorded an important visitor to the park in the *Butley Priory Chronicle*. On 11 September 1548, Mary Tudor (Henry VIII's sister), Dowager Queen of France and Duchess of Suffolk, journeyed to Staverton. She hunted foxes and had a picnic lunch 'with cheerful, laughing gentry under the oaks.'

By 1601 the park had changed hands once again, and was owned by Sir Michael Stanhope, who commissioned John Norden to produce the first ever detailed survey of the area, which is still in existence. This shows the park 'well wooded' with sheep paths, heathland and many features which can be seen on the present day map of the farm.

During the 17th century, after the production of Norden's map, several areas of the park were cleared and cropped, reducing the area of woodland to roughly its present size of 280 acres. An account of 1607 indicates more new building being undertaken on the estate, and that 'men from Hollesley were provided with 13 shillings and 4 pence worth of beer, bread and beef, when they carried timber from the park.'

In all, the picture at this time is of the new landowner investing heavily in his new estate and relying to a substantial degree on the resources that the park presented. After this time the story of the park is one of diminishing size and economic importance as a woodland.

At some time during the 1700s a large circular table was made from Staverton oak for a banquet held at Orford Castle for the Marquis of Hartford (a friend of the Prince Regent), which is still to be found in the castle today.

Kirby, in 1764, recorded that pollarding was continuing at a slower pace for the production of fuel, with sheep grazing taking precedence. By the mid-1800s pollarding had ceased, and the park was sub-divided by hawthorn hedges. One of these sub-divisions is now called The Thicks, which contains many hollies dating from about this time. The hollies were never really recorded until 1819 when Cornwall wrote about 'hollies in great quantities, a beautiful sight in winter.'

The park was only lightly grazed in the 19th century, which accounts for the development of the scrub layer, with birch and rowan also colonising. The Thicks is an area of extraordinary growth, where the hollies are thriving and now dominating the oaks. The tallest holly tree in the British Isles was recorded here in the 1970s at a height of 73ft 9in, and a girth of 7ft 9in. This tree is thought to have fallen victim to the great storm of 1987, but several hollies still standing have girths in excess of 8ft, so they may well be taller.

In 1900 sheep grazing stopped altogether, with the park and The Thicks being used as a game reserve. Since then the vegetation has not altered greatly. While shooting in Staverton Park in the 1930s, King George V's game cart hit and damaged one of the ancient oaks, and, writing of the incident to his hosts, he expressed the wish that every effort be made to save the sacred tree, which can still be seen today.

From 1939 to 1945 Staverton Park was used as a military camp for tank exercises and trials for developing the 'Funnies,' a machine which had many uses including the breaching of enemy sea defences. A visit of inspection by King George VI was recorded in photographs that can be found in the Bovington Tank Museum. Also during World War Two, two aircraft crashed into the park, one German and one Canadian, burning a large clearing in the wood.

In 1946 Jack Kemball took over at Wantisden, and in 1982, due to excessive surrounding crop damage, 50 acres of park were again enclosed for the wild fallow deer. Red deer have subsequently been introduced to the park. Today Staverton Park is a Site of Special Scientific Interest (SSSI). It has an abundance of unusual animals and plants, but the most important residents are invertebrates, fungi and lichens, some of which are found nowhere else.

The Kemballs – a family that put little known Wantisden on the map

The old-time song should have recorded that 'the Kemballs are coming' (not the Campbells), for such a dynasty has added greatly to the history of a hitherto little known corner of Suffolk, the parish of Wantisden, near Woodbridge.

During nearly 60 years' occupation of farmland and a unique area of

ancient woodland, three generations of the Kemball family have made
huge improvements in agricultural production, conservation and leisure
facilities, in an area once ravaged by preparations for war. The man who
started it all, Mr Jack Kemball, is the family's senior member and their
inspiration. Revered by farmers throughout the county, he has a golden
smile and hands that, in 2003, could still handle the controls of earth-
moving equipment at the age of 92.

It was wonderful to meet the family again as I made my third visit to
the Wantisden estate in 11 years. My first visit to the 16th-century
Wantisden Hall, in 1992, was to interview Jack as he prepared to take
centre stage as President of the Suffolk Show. The second occasion, four
years later, was to publicise the family's forthcoming first Power of the
Past event, but the scope of the interview at Dale Farm with Jack, son Bill
and Bill's wife, Jane, the three partners in Wantisden Hall Farms Estate
Ltd, was widened for a two-week family farms feature, published on
consecutive Saturdays in the *East Anglian Daily Times*.

It was to Dale Farm that I returned in the summer of 2003 for an
update on the family businesses, and to meet the same three family
members to discuss changes during the last seven years. The principal
changes were those of advancement through the purchase in 2001 of a
large part of the former USAF Bentwaters air base, which adjoins their

*The Kemball family
enjoying a picnic
among the ancient
trees in Staverton Park.*

farmland, and the development of a large conference centre and leisure complex for weddings, dinner dances, hunt balls and the like, known as Wantisden Valley. More about that later.

The Wantisden story began with Jack Kemball having continued a family tradition. He had a brother and two sisters, and their father, Charles, farmed at Cox Farm, Groton, near Hadleigh. Jack was a student at Chadacre Agricultural Institute, and afterwards became farm manager at Alfred Sainsbury's Hadleigh Estate. He remained there until the autumn of 1946, when he took over the Wantisden Estate, where a high proportion of the extensive heathland had been used for tank battle training during World War Two, in preparation for the D-Day landings.

A large part of income in the early years was derived from sales of rabbits. Jack gradually reclaimed approximately 900 acres out of a total of 1,700 acres at that time. The fact that it was light, sandy soil presented a number of problems from an agricultural point of view, the lack of rainfall always being a major concern, particularly in a dry year. The benefits of irrigation became obvious in the 1950s and 1960s, but it was not until 1972 that the construction of an extensive irrigation system was put into effect at Wantisden by Bill and his father. The benefits of the irrigation system were most keenly felt in the drought years of the mid-1970s. The need increased with root crop acreage, so lakes were established at two locations in natural valleys. Jack carried out the excavations himself with his hydraulic digger, while Bill took care of the landscaping. As Jane Kemball pointed out on a previous occasion, each generation of a family brings something new into farming. The contribution of the present younger generation has been considerable, including the use of computers and marketing; Jack and Bill sought improvement of light land cropping and brought this about through irrigation. Six-and-a-half miles of nine-inch underground mains were laid and three pumps totalling 600hp were installed. With a hydrant in each field, irrigation is supplied to the whole arable area from 50 acres of lakes. When there was a shortage of produce in the dry mid-1970s, the family was able to supply produce in both quantity and quality.

The third generation of the Kemballs is represented by Bill and Jane's son and three daughters. John, Sarah, Elizabeth (Bee) and Kate are all involved in the family businesses. Bee runs the Kemballs' other main business, Debach Enterprises, which provides warehousing and distribution services, the company having expanded operations at the family's main offices at Ransomes Euro Park, Ipswich (Bill and Jane are

Members of the Kemball family on a day out in Staverton Park, Wantisden, which is thought to have the largest collection of pollarded oaks in Europe.

also directors of this company); Sarah and John run Bentwaters Parks, and youngest daughter Kate is responsible for the Wantisden Valley diversification and the annual Power of the Past event.

The family are keen conservationists, and Wantisden Hall Farms Ltd became a LEAF (Linking Environment And Farming) in 1998, for a five-year term. The farm, managed by Mike Fielden, specialises in field vegetables, including sweetcorn, but the most important crop is potatoes. Over the years careful attention has been paid to varietal choice and the targeting of markets to maximise the farm's niche as a first and second early potato producer as well as a maincrop producer for long term on-farm storage. This has resulted in a varied portfolio of varieties enabling constant supply throughout the season.

Other crops include onions, which go for long-term storage ready to supply the supermarkets from January to June, and carrots for the fresh and processing sectors, and green beans. Sugar beet, malting barley and feed wheat are also grown.

Bill set up Debach Enterprises in June 1976 by purchasing the former mushroom farm at Clopton, near Woodbridge, part of the old Debach airfield. Originally, the idea was to operate a company or business not associated with agriculture. He and Jane thought it prudent to diversify at a time when farm incomes were reasonably good, rather than wait until an economic turndown, when others would be seeking diversification.

'Museum will salute dedication of bases'

This headline in the *East Anglian Daily Times* announced for the first time in July 2003 that the Kemball family were putting together a new museum dedicated to the history and personnel of the former American twin air bases of Bentwaters and Woodbridge.

The report by Richard Smith said that the newly-formed Bentwaters Aviation Society was developing the Bentwaters Cold War Museum in a former command bunker. At the invitation of Mr Bill Kemball, I visited Bentwaters – renamed Bentwaters Parks following the takeover of much of the airfield site by his family – a few days after the press announcement, and there I met the project leader, Sarah Kemball.

Why house it in a bunker? Sarah replied: 'We have a building which, to be honest, we can't use for anything else – a big concrete square with no windows – so it isn't a building that's likely to be used for any commercial purpose, and it seems the obvious place to have a museum. The command bunkers formed the nucleus of all Cold War bases during an alert.'

The aim was to have on show memorabilia based on the Cold War period from Bentwaters and Woodbridge. While the building was similar to all other Air Force base command bunkers, the use of special lighting, dressed models in uniform and historical photographs will recreate the times of 20 years ago.

Sarah said that American ex-service personnel sometimes visited the base while on holiday with their families, but were a little sad to see everything 'dead and gone,' especially across the road from the now quiet runways, where there used to be a

Debach Enterprises did begin with the storage of farm produce such as cereals, oilseed rape and sugar beet pulpnuts. Then, with increased production of grain in the early 1980s, the business was accepted by the Intervention Board to provide regional facilities for crop storage and laboratory testing. This gave Bill the opportunity to expand the business by acquiring storage facilities in Norfolk and at Felixstowe, Ipswich and Martlesham Heath. During this time, Bill acquired other sites in Ipswich which were tied in with contracts for the storage of products for the United States Air Force. It also coincided with the firm Ransomes, Sims and Jefferies at Ipswich pulling out of agricultural machinery production. As the Kemballs were at that time occupying part of the factory, they had the opportunity to buy 220,000 square feet of buildings on 12 acres of land now known as Ransomes Euro Park. Debach Enterprises became a company in 1985 when transport and distribution of a wide range of hospital, school, shops and other amenities. 'They find it quite strange,' she said.

I took the opportunity to visit the empty weather station in the control tower, where my ex-service American son-in-law, Sgt Paul Gross, had performed his duties as a weather observer. The photographs that were later sent to him over the Internet would no doubt be hardly recognisable as the room buzzing with the activity of a very busy base that

The former control tower of the disused Bentwaters American Air Force base, now in the ownership of the Kemball family.

he remembers. For Paul and for the many thousands of USAF personnel who served on the base, there is a need to consider an appeal by Sarah Kemball for any form of memorabilia of their time on the base. It is hoped that the contents of the museum will include scale models of every plane to have been stationed at the twin air bases, building up a history linking their activities to worldwide events.

Bentwaters Parks Ltd, the company set up by the Kemball family, has funded some of the costs and the aviation society has been seeking sponsorship.

products was introduced into the business. Today, the company occupies more than 750,000 sq ft of high-quality bonded warehouse facilities, with controlled environment pallet racking, computerised stock control, and many other facilities.

Wantisden Valley is where people meet for business and leisure – and to get married

Wantisden Valley, an area almost hidden from view to travellers in the Orford area of east Suffolk, has in recent times become an important business conference venue and both a corporate and leisure entertainment centre, after years of careful planning and development by the Kemball family. At its heart is the mediaeval woodland known as Staverton Park, a conservation area steeped in history, going back to the Domesday Book, and of interest to anyone who appreciates wildlife.

On the edge of the park is Shepherds Cottage, an 18th-century thatched building licensed for civil marriage ceremonies. The cottage, which can seat up to 30 people for dinner, overlooks the family's deer park, containing red and fallow deer. Extensive lakes nearby have been developed, to encourage nesting birds by the development of small islands out of reach of predators such as foxes.

Converted brick barns with original features such as flint walls and interior beams have rooms of varying sizes catering for conferences and other functions for between 20 and 500 people. The doors of the main

At Wantisden, the Kemball family has established a countryside venue for weddings and conferences, accommodating parties of 20 to 500 people.

Inside one of the various rooms used for functions at Wantisden.

barn allow access for large vehicles and items, useful for trade fairs, product launches, exhibitions and auctions. The facility is licensed for wedding services, reception dinners, dinner dances and charity balls.

Mrs Jane Kemball tells an amusing story of when Tesco personnel came to Wantisden Valley, because they had grown potatoes in a trial and wanted somewhere to test them. 'We incorporated this with a farm trip so that they could see the conservation side of the farm,' she said. They had their conference in the cottage, and then a chef came from London to cook the potatoes, which the Tesco representatives tasted. This was followed by a clay pigeon shoot the following day, making a pleasant way to end a two-day event organised for them by her daughter Kate, on behalf of a potato producer.

'They were so pleased with the arrangement that they said they were going to get six or seven top chefs to come out to the country to see where and how English potatoes are grown, and also see the environmentally friendly side of the farm. One little part of the farm had helped another part, but it was interesting to me to discover that people from London had never ever seen a potato grown. It's like going back to the days of the war!'

Jane's husband, Bill, added that it was fair to say, in general, that the farm is used quite a lot by major retailers, such as Tesco, Sainsbury and others, as an example of how intensive agriculture can run well alongside conservation.

Nostalgia the key at Wantisden's Power of the Past weekend

To host an annual exhibition, providing farming folk with nostalgia and non-farming folk with a glimpse of a vanished world of true horsepower, traction engines and early examples of agricultural 'prime movers' at Wantisden, near Orford, is the realised dream of the Kemball family.

The idea for a new weekend event in the Suffolk rural social calendar, which would also benefit local charities, was developed as a direct result of the family having hosted a ploughing day in 1995. The first Power of the Past was held in late September of the following year, and was an instant success.

Every year since then, Power of the Past has been meticulously planned on an ever grander scale, with the eighth event being held in September 2003. Plans are well advanced for the ninth in the autumn of 2004. The events so far have now raised close to £100,000 for local charities.

I attended the very first event, shortly before my retirement from the

How Bentwaters air base got its name – to avoid confusion

The name Bentwaters is said to derive from a pair of cottages known as the Bentwaters Cottages. Once situated not far from Wantisden Church, the cottages have long since been demolished. Mr Bill Kemball said the majority of the airfield is in the parish of Wantisden, but it was thought that if the name Wantisden was chosen for the base it would be confused with another Suffolk airfield, RAF Wattisham, and it was decided use the name of the farm cottages instead.

There are apparently two theories as to why the cottages were called Bentwaters in the first place, as their origins go a long way back in the past. 'One thing is definite', said Bill, 'that is the well which served the cottages was at the bottom of quite a deep pit'. One theory is that the well was bent, because sometimes brick-built wells used to twist. Bill's father, Mr Jack Kemball, added that often with twisted wells it was not possible to see the bottom from the top. The other theory is that there was a steep, winding path which went down to the well. However, the well has since been found to be straight, so the second theory seems more likely.

Bentwaters was a Royal Air Force base during World War Two and the RAF remained there until 1949, about the time the cottages were demolished. There was

EADT, and took a number of photographs which have remained unpublished until now. With more than 20,000 people attending the most recent events, attractions have increased in line with the expectations of a paying public. Children are being catered for in a very big way, with the provision of a Big Wheel, galloper roundabouts, Wall of Death and many other fairground rides that have been enjoyed by youngsters for generations.

Power of the Past is one of a limited number of events in the region to feature the working capabilities of the Suffolk Punch, one of the oldest heavy horse breeds in the world. Their displays of pulling power have proved popular with the crowds. These sturdy animals were in the forefront of traditional methods of ploughing, drilling and cultivating, and are also used to demonstrate shoeing, grooming and harnessing.

Until 50 years ago, heavy horses were still working on the farms of East Anglia, but the progress of mechanisation, especially during World War Two, led to the rapid replacement of horsepower by tractors and other mechanical equipment. The heavy horse breeds (Shire, Percheron, Suffolk and Clydesdale) nearly died out but were maintained for shows by a few enthusiasts. Other enthusiasts collected disused horse-drawn

then a three-year gap, when Jack Kemball cultivated part of the airfield site and used one of the hangars to house agricultural machinery. This continued until the arrival of the Americans in 1952, and the Kemballs say they have gone full circle, using the very same hangar to house farm machinery once again.

Said Bill Kemball: 'We have identified precisely where the cottages were and we have found the pit. What we would like to do is re-excavate to establish where the properties were. We know approximately where they were, but need to do more excavations to locate the footings. This is just for interest's sake, so that we can definitely say where the cottages stood.'

As far as nearby Walnut Tree Farm is concerned, the buildings were demolished in the late 1950s, and the family have found all the footings for the house and farm buildings. The well on that site is still there. All the information and subsequent revelations will be made available in the airfield museum.

A view from the tower of part of the airfield which has reverted back to agricultural use.

equipment and restored it to working condition, as demonstrated at Power of the Past. The harness in use is a mixture of old pieces still in good condition, and new harness that is still made by those who continue the skills.

The Kemball family name is emblazoned on one of the many steam giants taking part in the first Power of the Past event at Wantisden in 1996.

Displays of military vehicles, including a 100-tonne tank, have also proved popular with visitors. For the first time, in 2003, Power of the Past had a display of living vans on show, These vans were mainly used by crews of contract threshing and road-making gangs who would move from site to site often many miles from home. Sometimes called sleeping vans, they provided accommodation for two to six men with a cook boy to prepare their meals. The vans were built by most of the leading traction engine and steam roller manufacturers.

In addition to the agricultural attractions, there is always ample room under cover, accommodating numerous stands in a large craft area. There are also full catering facilities.

Another large steam engine belches distinctive smoke from its chimney at the event.

Crafts such as rag-rug making were displayed at the Power of the Past event in 1996, and have become a regular feature.

A craftswoman at the spinning wheel produces the thread that others will use in fine craftwork.

Rural domestic crafts are varied, and another example is this beautiful sample from the cake decoration exhibition.

A 1918 Robey portable engine duplex cylinder belonging to W.J. Kemball, at the Power of the Past event in 2003.

*Recreating the days
when farm work
required plenty of
personal skill and real
horsepower out in the
fields.*

Following the plough: two small boys enjoy watching this small prime mover being put through its paces.

Stopping for a chat during a working demonstration at the first Power of the Past weekend organised by the Kemball family at Wantisden.

Farrier Vincent
Buckman gives a
demonstration of
shoeing a Suffolk
Punch.

The Gallopers
roundabout, a
favourite of many
attending the 2003
Power of the Past
event.

An outside view of the
Wall of Death
daredevil motorbike
ride, once seen at
funfairs throughout the
country.

Machinery enthusiasts enjoy discussion of cultivation equipment.

Machinery giants of yesterday line up at the 2003 Power of the Past exhibition.

CHAPTER 5

Lodge Farm, Westhorpe, near Stowmarket

The farms of Westhorpe, near Stowmarket, have an honoured place in the royal history of Tudor England. Much of the land today farmed by the Barker family was part of the the huge Westhorpe Hall estate of Charles Brandon, Duke of Suffolk. He was the second husband of still teenage Princess Mary Tudor, daughter of King Henry VII and Elizabeth of York, younger sister of King Henry VIII and dowager Queen of France after a brief marriage to King Louis XII.

West Thorpe, in Anglo-Saxon times, was on the west border of the Hundred of Hartismere (a tax administrative district). It had status and importance even then. At the time of the Domesday Book in 1086, Westhorpe had 31 small-holdings of three to seven acres. A population of 190 souls was more than the number in the village today. Common land was once shared out in strips, and four of these are still in the Westhorpe parish. The Barkers have two of them, both on Crown Farm, dating back to 1275.

In the 16th century, the period of greatest interest to the parish, the Barker family's principal farmhouse, Lodge Farm, was then the hunting lodge for the deer park belonging to one of Suffolk's most historical estate houses, the large, moated Westhorpe Hall. Although the imposing architectural property assured Brandon's popularity locally and at the court of Henry VIII, it has long since vanished having been pulled down in the middle of the 18th century.

Brandon, who was created the first of Henry's parvenu peers, built property to demonstrate his greatness to contemporaries. He was also unusual in the number of houses he built, undertaking four major enterprises and several minor ones. Westhorpe Hall, which had 16 principal rooms and a chapel with stained-glass windows, was said to have cost him £12,000, a huge sum in those days.

Charles Brandon's father was killed at the Battle of Bosworth in 1485, and Henry VII is thought to have adopted the infant Charles and brought him up with his own children. As an adult, Charles became a close friend of Henry VIII, often meeting him in jousting combat.

After a series of battles with the French, Henry VIII sent off his beautiful and charming young sister, Mary, to be married to the French king, Louis XII. Louis was 53 years old, an 'infirm and gouty widower,' and Mary was a reluctant teenager of 17. She only agreed to the marriage, in October 1514, on condition that she could choose her second husband herself. King Louis died, exhausted, three months later.

Lodge Farm, Westhorpe, once part of the great Westhorpe Hall Estate of Charles Brandon, Duke of Suffolk.

Brandon was despatched by Henry to bring Mary home but, instead, they married in secret in Paris in February 1515, risking the wrath of Henry and Cardinal Wolsey when they returned to England. Many back home even feared for Brandon's life. The king was furious, but spared him, and a public wedding took place later after the furore died down. Brandon's punishment was a 'fine' of £24,000, to be paid off in instalments. The Duke's good fortune continued when the manor of Westhorpe came to him during the same year that he took his royal bride.

The *Archaeological Journal* of the Royal Archaeological Institute (volume 145), published in 1988, reports that the Crown's complex dealings with the de la Pole family caused Westhorpe to pass, at the death of Margaret de la Pole, dowager Countess of Suffolk, to Robert Washington, serjeant-at-arms. According to the record: 'The reversion had been granted to Brandon, and while he was absent in France in February, his councillors bought out Washington for £300, as they did the Marquis of Dorset and the Earl of Shrewsbury at nearby Wyverstone and Walsham.' With other manors, these formed the most westerly of the Duke's three main blocks of estates in the county.

Westhorpe was the symbol of the Duke's coming-of-age as an East Anglian magnate to rival Thomas Howard, Duke of Norfolk. It was there, for example, that Brandon aimed to exercise the lavish hospitality which was so important to his local standing.

Mary Tudor let it be known that she preferred to be known as the Queen of France, but as the Duke and Duchess of Suffolk, she and Brandon were themselves lavishly entertained on many of the larger estates in the county, among them, as recalled elsewhere, Staverton Park, Wantisden, where they hunted and picnicked under the oak trees; Butley Priory, where illness-plagued Mary rested for several weeks at a time; and, while visiting Butley, she would call on her friend, Sir John Glemham at nearby Glemham Hall, near Saxmundham.

Regretfully for Brandon, Westhorpe's greatest moment of prominence was also to be its saddest. Mary, who bore Brandon four children, was frequently unwell during her final years, and used her last reserves of

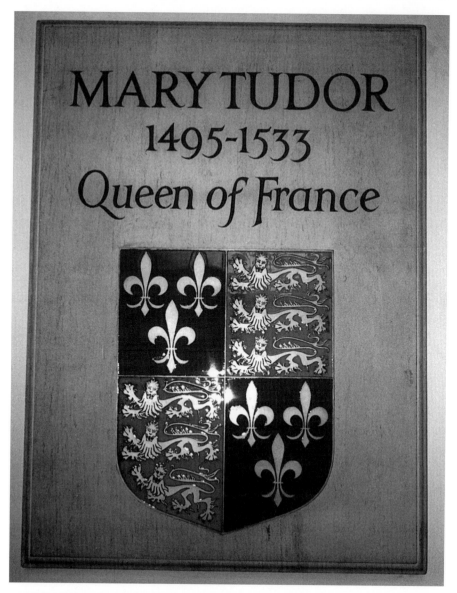

Plaque above the grave of Princess Mary Tudor in St Mary's Church, Bury St Edmunds.

energy preparing for the wedding of their daughter, Frances. The distraught Duke made one final visit to his wife's bedside during her illness, but had to return to London to supervise the arrangements for Anne Boleyn's coronation, scheduled for 1 June. In fact, Suffolk directed the whole show, from the Queen's entry into the Tower on the eve of her procession through London, to supervising the arrangements for a great banquet in Westminster Hall, where 800 people sat down to dine on courses which included around 30 separate dishes.

Mary, far away, bodily and in spirit, from all her brother's marriage celebrations, died in seclusion on 25 June 1533, still in her 37th year – some say still shocked by the news that her brother the King had secretly married Anne, who was carrying his child.

There was no court mourning for Mary. Her husband, exhausted from his own efforts organising Anne Boleyn's triumph as part of his duties as Lord High Steward, made a further hurried visit to Westhorpe, then

Another plaque to the memory of Princess Mary Tudor. A plain burial stone marks her final resting place.

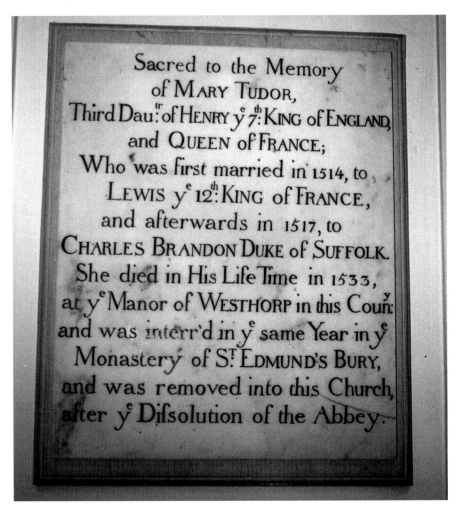

returned to London – it was not the custom for a husband to attend his wife's funeral.

Though her entrails were reportedly buried in Westhorpe Church, Mary was accorded a send-off befitting her English and French royal status. Her body was embalmed, and in its lead coffin was removed to the cloistered chapel which adjoined the house. Here it remained for three weeks with lighted tapers constantly burning around it, and mass said every day. After a final requiem mass on Tuesday 21 July, attended by Lady Frances Brandon, her eldest daughter, the mourners breakfasted in the great chamber. Then the coffin, richly draped in black velvet and bearing Mary's coat-of-arms, was taken out to a waiting carriage, drawn by six black horses, also clad in velvet, for the 14-mile journey to Bury St Edmunds.

The elaborate funeral procession was led by 100 yeomen in black gowns, each carrying a wax taper for lighting at the conclusion of the journey. These were followed by clergy, knights, barons, gentlemen and officers of the household. Then came the carriage, followed by Mary's daughter, Lady Frances, the chief mourner, and on her right-hand side, riding, her new husband, the Marquis of Dorset. Behind came an enormous following of noblemen and women, all attended by a servant. Last of all came the yeomen and servants connected with the estates, all dressed in black. They reached Bury in the early afternoon and were met at the Abbey gate by the abbot and priests. From the outer gate to the high altar, everywhere was draped in black cloth, and all the wax tapers were lit. Later there was a banquet in the great hall followed by an all-night vigil. The following day, after four solemn masses, the body was placed in a sepulchre. When the ceremony was over, a great pall of cloth of gold was placed over the tomb.

After the Dissolution of the Monasteries, Mary Tudor's body was removed from the Abbey and re-interred in nearby St Mary's Church, where it rests, on the north side of the altar, under a very plain stone. An inscription was added and, according to the wishes of King Edward VII, coping was placed around it, 'to keep off intruders' feet.'

According to the Royal Archaeological Institute journal, the wife who had enabled Suffolk to build his house was no sooner dead than his possession of it was threatened. In the debt settlement which followed, King Henry demanded the reversion to Westhorpe if the Duke were to die without male heirs. To guarantee this, the manor and house were transferred to the Crown in 1535. Finally, in the wake of the Lincolnshire

revolt of 1536, when Henry wanted Brandon to concentrate his energies
on governing that county, the King began to negotiate the exchange of all
the Duke's East Anglian estates for an increased endowment in
Lincolnshire. Suffolk was eventually persuaded to move his entire
household to Lincolnshire.

The journal notes that 'In 1538 the park at Westhorpe held 100 Red
deer and 200 Fallow deer'. The park was noted for providing 'ffyne
ffedynge grounde,' and the gardens were said to be 'extensive and
designed in the French manner.' The house was kept in repair for a while,
more than £50 being spent in 1545, but in the following year the kitchens
were stripped and a brewing vessel, eight stoves and three ovens were sold
off.

Westhorpe was granted to Anne of Cleves, and at her death was passed
to Sir Thomas Cornwallis, but it does not seem to have been inhabited,
except perhaps by lessees, and was pulled down, though apparently still
sound, in about 1750. It may have been too large for anyone other than
Suffolk to live there, so it was a fitting, if ironic, tribute to his power and
influence on one of England's most flamboyant monarchs.

Thomas Martin, an eye witness to the demolition, was not at all
pleased at what he saw:

> ...*The workmen are now pulling it down as fast as may be, in a
> very careless and injudicious manner. The coping bricks,
> battlements and many other ornamental pieces are made of earth
> and burnt hard, and are as fresh as when first built and might
> have been taken down whole (if care had been taken), but all the
> fine chimneys and ornaments were pull'd down with ropes, and
> crush'd to pieces in a shameful manner. There was a monstrous
> figure of Hercules, sitting cross-legg'd with a club and lyon beside
> him, but all shattered to pieces, and the painted glass is likely to
> share the same fate.*

Today, very little survives of Charles Brandon's great house. A brick
bridge crosses the moat of the west side of the site and the moat turns at
right angles on the north and south sides, and brick walls and buttresses
are visible in places on the south and west sides.

The following were notes made by David Barker to enlighten visitors
going around the farm on special occasions: 'A recent archaeological dig
revealed the site of the porter's house over the bridge which had a stone
floor and 18-inch thick stone walls; also revealed was the chalk floor of

The three-arch bridge once used by Mary Tudor to go in and out of husband Charles Brandon's magnificent Westhorpe Hall.

The residential care home that now stands on the site of Westhorpe Hall.

the courtyard. The bridge dates from this period and has Brandon's badge on the other side of a lion's head with a ducal coronet.

'In 1990 the first phase of a four-year programme began to clean out and restore the moat to its Tudor size. A vast number of bottles dating back 100 years were discovered in the section on the far side of the house. These are now in the family museum. In 1991 on the inside of the moat we discovered the foundations of the original hall and pieces of decorative terracotta from the walls of the old hall. Under the silt we found pieces of Tudor pottery. With the help of Suffolk County Council's archaeological department, we were able to draw to scale the original foundations of the hall. The fattening pigs are kept at Hall Farm. The old barn (listed) is built of timbers from the original hall.'

Living through an agricultural revolution of immense proportions

The sequence of events which brought the Barker family to occupy land of historical importance at Westhorpe was almost accidental. It was certainly fortuitous. The intriguing story is told by David Barker, who was born at Hall Farm, Langham, where the family lived until 1957. He believes there are few families more 'Suffolk orientated.'

Their move in the 1950s from Langham, some five miles away, to Westhorpe was precipitated by Tom Blackwell, of the famous food firm Crosse and Blackwell. Tom, a wealthy man who owned Langham Hall, had for some considerable time tried to buy the Barkers' farm. 'Father [Eric] kept saying no, but in the spring of '57, Tom offered £21,000 for the 240–250 acres of Hall Farm, which was mixed land and included quite a lot of woodland. It was way over the odds, so my parents sold it at that time, but they then had to look at different farms to move on to in order to vacate in the October of that year.' Eric and Ella Barker looked around for a few months but couldn't find anything they wanted to buy and, in despair, they even started to think about finding a house to live in until they could locate a suitable farm.

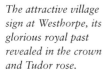

The attractive village sign at Westhorpe, its glorious royal past revealed in the crown and Tudor rose.

Fortunately, the 330 acres of Lodge, Moat and Appletree Farms at Westhorpe came under the hammer at the old Everards Hotel in Bury St Edmunds, a building long since gone. 'Father went to the auction having viewed it only once, and then not with any real intention of buying. He took with him Tom Ashton, of Bankes Ashton. 'There was a deathly hush as the auctioneer attempted to get a bid from those present, saying that the farm *had* to be sold. Father finally put a bid in for £15,000 for the 330 acres. The auctioneer looked around, as they do and, as I quoted at my mother's funeral, he took a bid off a fly going up the wall, of £16,000. Father came back with further bid of £17,000 and to his amazement, the auctioneer reiterated that the farm *had* to be sold, and that he would sell it. He announced: 'Once, twice, three times' – and knocked it down to him. Father had bought 330 acres at Westhorpe for £47 10 shillings per acre.'

'Tom Ashton said to him, "Eric, you will never see farm land as cheap as that again." Mother wasn't at the sale, and when he returned home, he simply told her he had bought the farm at Westhorpe. She was aghast, and said she hadn't even looked at the house. Father told her: "I bought it so cheap, if you don't like the house I'll build you a new one." Having sold one farm for £21,000 and bought another, larger farm for £17,000, the £4,000 worth of capital was quite sufficient for that.'

The farm itself was not in particularly good condition, the heavy land needed a lot of drainage. 'It had huge hedges, all overgrown. The previous owner had a problem because I don't think he was ever able to generate the funds to keep within the business. Because it was a limited company, money seemed to be siphoned off because it was needed elsewhere, so he was always up against it.'

There were about 80 acres of sugar beet in the ground when Eric Barker took possession in the October, and it was quite a job getting the crop out of the ground. It was certainly a young person's farm, and Eric was then in his early thirties. One person told him bluntly: 'It's broke two people – and it will break you.'

But Eric was not going to be beaten. He bought a Track Marshall and plough for £1,000, and set to work. 'Within four years of buying Westhorpe Lodge Farms, the Shave family, who owned Westhorpe Hall Farm, came and asked him to buy their farm. So father bought 240 acres of Westhorpe Hall for £68 per acre, doubling his farm enterprise in four years, to around 570 acres. The agreement was that the Shave family could continue to live in the farmhouse for as long as they wanted, and it's the existing hall that we have now.'

In 1966, the Barkers bought 80 acres of West Farm for a price in the region of £240–£250 an acre, and then Green Farm was purchased the following year for nearly £300 an acre. So within a decade at Westhorpe, land under the family's control had risen to some 730 acres, at a time when there was a lot of government support for agriculture.

The late Eric and Ella Barker in the garden at Lodge Farm, Westhorpe.

It was also at this time that David and his elder brother, Roy, came into the family business. 'There was still this "Dig for Victory" slogan ringing in our ears, and it wasn't long after rationing had taken place. But by then things had begun to change. Back in 1957 there were some 11 farm holdings in the parish of Westhorpe – enabling 11 farmers and their wives, and perhaps 15 or 16 farm workers, to live off the land – basically 25 to 30 families whose livelihoods were sourced by farming.

'Today it is very different. Effectively there are two farm holdings in Westhorpe, one also doing contract farming outside the parish, and probably four family members working on it, and on our own holdings, there is Roy and myself and our wives, and we employ four people, two on pigs and two on arable. The rest of it, as far as all those farm holdings in 1957 are concerned, has gone.'

The type of farming in the 1950s was also very different to today. The milk would have been sent to the local creamery in Stowmarket or Bury St Edmunds, returning to the local area for retail sale. A lot of potatoes and other vegetables also would have been grown and sourced locally. 'There would have been slaughterhouses at Elmswell and Old Newton, and others serving butchers in the surrounding area, so farm animals would only have had to travel short distances. There would have been some six dairy herds in the area – now there are no dairy herds at all. There were perhaps five sheep flocks, and probably every one of the 11 holdings would have had a few pigs and chickens.

'When we talk about the environment, the average field size would probably be 10 acres, with big hedges and a lot of grassland, because farms would have just moved out of the horsepower era. Tractors had only just taken over from the horse, and there would be grassland and undrained agricultural land that was very difficult to farm. The whole of the post-war government agricultural policies were aimed at grant-aiding farmers to increase production. Draining wetland and enlarging fields for the machinery was all part and parcel of that process.'

A decade later, in 1967, the family took on David's grandfather's farm of 250 acres at Great Ashfield, taking the land under their control to around 1,000 acres. The next purchase was in 1980 when Church Farm, Westhorpe, was acquired. 'We tried to buy it privately, but it went to auction and we paid £1,800 per acre. In 1984 we bought a further 40 acres at Great Ashfield for £100,000, a piece of land that fell perfectly

Roy Barker (right) and staff of the Lodge Farm estate. Photograph taken by the author in 1996.

into the original farm. Grandfather had been trying all his life to buy it, and he was 84 years of age when we did buy it, and he was chuffed to bits.

'Times were hard in agriculture in the fifties and sixties. We had sacks to deal with, and people don't realise how difficult it was to lift sugar beet out by hand. Everything was manual labour. When in 1961 we were having terrible problems lifting beet on this very heavy land, we had two tractors pulling one trailer and ruts were literally more than a foot deep. I remember one of the old boys on the farm coming up to us in 1961, and father saying: "Well, Jessie, that's the last year I'm going to grow sugar beet." Old Jessie, laughing in disbelief, replied: "Yer, yer. That's what you said last year." Father said: "Yes, Jessie, but this year I mean it."

'It was true, we stopped growing sugar beet in 1961, and later, when I was chairman of Suffolk NFU and had to sit in on the county sugar beet committee, I rather tongue-in-cheek announced that my father stopped growing sugar beet in 1961, and that we had never regretted it. The committee members all looked up at me and probably thought, "What sort of county chairman have we got here? He's not going to be much help to sugar beet growers."

'We have instead concentrated on herbage seed, and have grown grass seeds all the time since. On this land, a two-year grass break is incredibly important to putting texture and structure back into the soil. We have maintained that specialised market of growing grass seeds right from the 1960s, and we are still doing that today.' Of the two types of varieties being grown, one is the agricultural *Aberdart*, which was described by David in glowing terms, adding: 'Animals like it because it is succulent compared to the old grass seeds'. Amenity varieties also being grown are those being used on the outfield of Lords cricket ground and top football pitches, and there is a good chance that some of their seeds have ended up on Ipswich Town's award-winning Portman Road pitch.

Looking back on his own agricultural experience, David says that the seventies, eighties and nineties, right up to 1997, were the 'fun' years to be in farming, but post-1997, it had been 'pretty damned tough,' a time when not much money was made. With a strong pound, governments hadn't had much interest in farmers, and in 1997, the strength of the pound totally undermined grain prices. In 1992, wheat was £120 per tonne, yet a decade later the price had slumped to £58 per tonne, having halved in actual terms. However, in 2003, because of a weakening pound and because of difficult harvests and droughts abroad, UK farmers saw an improvement in grain prices for both reasons. Grain quality had been 'fantastic' thanks to a hot, dry summer, while drying costs were very low.

There has been a big change since the seventies, when the emphasis was on growing spring barley. Technology in agriculture has moved on and Westhorpe was, more realistically, wheat-growing land, the crop in most years averaging three-and-a-half tonnes per acre. 'During the buoyant period, when wheat was making good money, obviously it was the basis not just of farming in Westhorpe but right across the county of Suffolk, which has in the region of half a million acres sown to winter wheat.'

Like many of the region's farmers, David Barker does not want to see GM (genetically modified) crops being grown here. 'I don't see the benefits,' he says. 'The winners in GM tend to be the big companies. I am not sure that it has been targeted to help farming or the environment.'

The Barkers continue to grow barley because they still have a pig enterprise, so they use it for straw and to feed the animals. However, they have changed in recent years to utilise more break crops because, with the reduced price of wheat, second and third wheat crops don't yield or pay as well. The break crops in the 2003 harvest year included some 100 acres of naked oats, a product which, surprisingly, is the foundation in the

David Barker (left) with staff in the sow house at Lodge Farm in 1996.

production of rat poison. The reason for this is that it is oily for absorption and therefore cost-effective.

In the 2003 harvest year, the Barker family was farming a total of some 1,250 acres, of which there are 600 acres of winter wheat; 100 acres of winter barley; 150 acres of herbage seed split between the two types, agricultural and amenity; 80 acres of peas, 50–60 acres of beans; 100 acres of naked oats, and some 100 acres of land set-aside to comply with regulations brought in by the European Union in 1992–93.

David believes that belonging to the European Union has had a major impact on UK farming, but not always for the best, he says. He considers farming in the 21st century to be more proscriptive in terms of form-filling and regulations which, he feels, would have been 'laughed out of court' in the 1960s. These include the climate change levy, which means filling in more forms in order to get some sort of help against the impact of climate change. 'That's the world we live in, and we can't necessarily do too much about it,' he said with a deep sigh of resignation. You just have to be one step ahead of the rules and regulations, it's much easier for young people to deal with the industry today than people who have been stuck in it for 30 or 40 years.'

Looking at today's family farming situation philosophically, David said: 'I suppose we have remained one of the truly mixed family farms. All the farms in the parish would have been like that back in the 1950s, but today, although not an oddity or a rarity, mixed family farms do not exist in the same proportion as they did even 10 years ago. There is much more contract farming and big areas without any livestock. There are fewer people working on farms, bigger machines to cover bigger areas; all very efficient, but it's also what the squeeze on agricultural incomes has done.'

At Westhorpe, they purchased a new drill in 2003 which is regarded as a fantastic piece of equipment. 'It goes well over the land and drills the grain spot-on, and it has even got the facility to increase the seed rate over rougher ground and, where there is a good seed bed, to reduce the seed rate. These are increased levels of technology.'

In contrast, David recalls unhappy days when workers were up to their knees in mud, attempting to pull every sugar beet out of the ground. To do that work now, there are six-row machines which 'flow' across the crop and harvest a whole field of beet in half a day. 'The old boys would have been gobsmacked,' he says. 'I met one the other day who said: "I'd have been sacked if I'd harvested a field like that. And with the amount

David Barker photographed in the driveway of Lodge Farm in 1996.

of beet that machine left behind, I would have been two times sacked on the spot!"

'When you compare the 1950s to the present day, there is no doubt that we have been through an agricultural revolution of immense proportions, starting out with horsepower and, 50 years later, we are looking at the present technology level of pea viners, sugar beet harvesters and combine harvesters. I can't believe that agriculture could change quite so dramatically ever again, over that same period of time. It has been a most remarkable change, and maybe some people might say we are very fortunate. I am sure we are.'

Looking back at what he terms 'spin-offs' from the countryside, David believes that every one of the farm holdings in Westhorpe in 1957 would have been an environmental oasis in its own right, with sheep, poultry and small birds living off the livestock areas and thick hedges around small fields. The main difference in the bird population then was that there were many more small farms with livestock, and livestock farms were the ones with lots of small birds. 'If you have cattle yards, you tend to get starlings and robins which are attracted by a great reservoir of insects. Whatever people say about the reduction in the number of small birds, the loss of livestock has been the biggest single factor. I don't think pesticides are necessarily to blame.'

Again, David cites rules and regulations as part of the problem, saying that, in these days of crop assurance, farmers, technically, have to keep sparrows out of their barns in case they allow salmonella to contaminate grain heaps. David admits, however, that some things have changed for the better. 'Farmers and workers used to heave sacks of corn weighing 16–18 stone (110 kilos or a ninth of a tonne) on their backs going up granary steps. That's really hard work and people don't always appreciate progress. When it comes to one-tonne buckets loading lorries, times really have changed.'

Hoarder who built up a valuable agricultural museum

'Don't throw anything away. It may be valuable some day.' Such advice of the past is being heeded in the 21st century as Britain becomes a nation of hoarders, no doubt encouraged by such popular television programmes as *Antiques Roadshow*.

The late Eric Barker began his own huge private collection of agricultural bygones almost half a century ago, when machines and implements no longer of use or were thrown out as rubbish. When I interviewed this very knowledgeable man a few years before he died, he took me on a guided tour of four large agricultural buildings where the hoarding had grown to gigantic proportions – and in retrospect, a truly rich heritage of engineering genius. Over the years, I met scores of farmers, throughout East Anglia, who were quite capable of perfecting their own inventions to enhance farming techniques.

Some of the hundreds of items of domestic farm kitchen equipment and agricultural implements in the Barker family museum.

I had a quick look inside each of these buildings simply to get the 'measure' of the collection, then we returned to each one in turn for more leisurely viewing. Collectively, the four buildings represented an Aladdin's cave of thousands of objects neatly arrayed on the floors, around the walls and on tables and benches. The assortment of items included odd-looking tools and implements of yesteryear: the uses for some could only be guessed at, and there were implements that would no doubt vex many of today's farmers.

There was such a lot to see that it proved difficult to concentrate on any particular object for long, so I had to settle for the 'butterfly' approach. Doubtless it was much the same for the hundreds of other visitors streaming into the buildings during special farming open days to raise funds for local church and village hall projects. This peep into a world gone by catered mainly for the over-60s organisations and machinery clubs, and many in their membership would have used the farming implements themselves at one time.

The collection was started in the 1950s with a Bentall horse-drawn plough, made at Maldon and used by Mr Barker's father and grandfather. He also used it himself to learn the craft. When horse ploughing was superceded by the tractor, Eric kept the plough for sentimental reasons. 'Then I found some more tools of father's, which had been grandfather's, and I started putting them together, and gradually built up a collection of all old bits and pieces,' he said.

Son David offered another point of view: 'He would be going to farm sales quite regularly in the 1970s and buying up farming bygones for an absolute knock-down price, because they were only going to be destroyed. When he came back, we used to say "What on earth has he brought back today?" An old vehicle would come into the yard absolutely filled up with junk. He kept acquiring old farming relics at a time when nobody was really interested in them.'

However, both David and Roy were happy to nurture their father's growing interest – and left him to it while they got on with the farming! David: 'It wasn't until the 1980s that others started to be aware of the value of these things. By that time he had got a vast collection and we were having to build more farm buildings to house it.'

The four buildings, which are fully protected against thieves, contain nearly 60 vintage tractors and a host of threshing machines, binders, sail reapers, mowers, wagons, carts and combine harvesters, as well as working horse equipment and implements. There are also tools used by

Some 60 prime movers of British and foreign manufacture in the Barker family's private museum.

blacksmiths, wheelwrights, carpenters and thatchers. In addition, there are barn, granary and field tools. Domestic items include dairy equipment, early washing machines, an early icebox refrigerator and kitchen utensils of every description.

While time only allowed for a brief glance at the more interesting features, the tour for me was still an exciting journey through time to chart the history and progress of mechanised agriculture. From perhaps even earlier times there is a collection of glass bottles of all shapes and sizes taken from the moat around old Westhorpe Hall. 'There were hundreds and hundreds of them, all just thrown in,' said Eric Barker. The representative collection on show includes three-corner shaped bottles specially made so that blind people could recognise more easily that they contained poison.

The oldest item in the museum is an axe or hammer head which was unearthed by harrows during work on the family's other farm at Great Ashfield. It was dated by the British Museum to 2,000 BC.

After seeing what looked like a large pin, I learned from my patient guide the true meaning of the oft-used expression 'pig in a poke.'

Apparently, farm workers generations ago hadn't many good clothes to wear, so they would wrap an old sack they called a poke around their shoulders to keep out the cold. A poke pin was used to keep the sack together. Some farmers allowed their workers to take home a piglet to put in a sty at the bottom of the garden. When the farm worker was going down the road at night, with a bulge in the poke over his shoulders, friends would stop and ask him if he had a pig in the poke. And that's where the saying came from.

Among regular visitors to the farm are schoolchildren, who are always fascinated by an old candling lamp that is lit, with an egg resting in its place on top. The light illuminates the egg to show whether there is a chick inside.

In the years before he died, Eric Barker found it much more difficult to obtain farming bygones, simply because more people were aware of their value and owners wanted, in old money terms, 'pounds, shillings and pence.' He was proud of the fact that much of the agricultural machinery in his display was made in East Anglia, including the famous Smythe seed drill. Also to be seen is a self-acting barley screen made in 1872 by R. Boby, of Bury St Edmunds, a company at one time renowned for such labour-saving seed equipment. The price new was £6 10 shillings. Other Suffolk-made drills include one by Youngs of Eye. 'The wheels were pulled right out so that they ran in the furrow,' said Eric. 'It required one horseman and one other man to steer the coulters.'

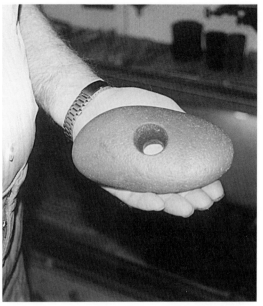

Ancient artefact: this axe or hammer head, found during field operations on the Barker family's other farm at Great Ashfield, was dated by the British Museum to 2,000 BC.

The huge line-up of tractors virtually fills one of the buildings. Eric, a man of character who is now greatly missed by so many of his own and succeeding generations, could not be certain of the exact number of items in the museum, but he said he would certainly know if there was something missing!

Footnote:

In a footnote to the story of his late father's huge private collection of agricultural artefacts, David Barker said 'The family museum has to a large extent been mothballed since father died in 1997. We haven't sold a great deal of it, but it's just so incredibly difficult now to

RANSOMES THRESHING MACHINE

manage a museum and farm at the same time, because of health and safety issues. You cannot now have a large number of visitors coming round a farm.

'Financially, too, it doesn't stack up, because you cannot afford to have someone looking after a museum like this because you never get the income. Father used to open the museum in the evenings for organised parties and machinery clubs to go round, and it helped to raise money for church funds and the village hall. The museum is still here, of course, but it is not open in the way it used to be.'

Keeping a straight line: Looking back to 1996 when Eric Barker gave the author a personal viewing of his museum and showed him this squaring board, an implement which was used in the furrow for accurate field work.

The late Eric and Ella Barker sitting in the recording studio where Eric saved for posterity archive film and video tape of events in Suffolk covering several decades.

Royal Mary — a central figure in Tudor Suffolk

A lock of hair belonging to Mary Tudor. Graham Portlock

MARY Tudor, daughter of King Henry VII, younger sister of King Henry VIII, dowager Queen of France and, latterly, wife of Charles Brandon, Duke of Suffolk, is a central figure of the Tudor period of these chronicles, having been associated with four of the farming estates featured.

Her Suffolk home and place of death in her mid-thirties was Westhorpe Hall, near Stowmarket, a great moated manor house built by Brandon. The land included a deer park, and its lodge farm is part of the land owned in modern times by the Barker family.

In 1516, while Duchess of Suffolk, Mary Tudor made the first of many visits to a place which became very dear to her heart – Butley Priory, today owned by Sir Edward Greenwell.

In August 1537 Mary, who as the widow of King Louis XII preferred to be addressed as Queen Mary, is recorded as having visited Sir John Glemham at Glemham Hall, near Saxmundham. A second hall, built on the same site in 1560, is owned by Major Philip Hope-Cobbold, who was born there.

On a glorious early summer day in June 1528, Mary travelled to Butley again, and from there she rode out to Staverton Park on a fox hunt, and 'dined under the oaks there with game and sport merry enough'. The beautiful old forest, then belonging to the priory, is now owned by the Kemball family of Wantisden, and is well preserved.

Mary Tudor, c.1514. Painted for King Louis XII before Mary left England for France to be his queen.

CHAPTER 6

Houghton Hall, Cavendish

The unique story of the Wise family, at historic Houghton Hall, on the edge of the picturesque village of Cavendish, is not only a truly Anglo-American one, starting with the courtship of Stephen and Mary that crossed the Atlantic, but also one that is littered with amazing coincidences.

The involvement of two Agricultural Attachés at the American Embassy in London, 35 years apart, has perhaps been the most amazing coincidence in the life of octogenarian Stephen Wise. The first one he met helped him to map out an important business tour of America, where he met wife-to-be Mary. The second became his daughter-in-law.

There is a further story to be told leading up to that happy American intervention. Stephen's father, Eugene, bought 15th-century Houghton Hall in 1938, and took possession early the following year with his family. The 500-acre holding was in a run-down state from the period of Depression, and at that time it was not easy to put the farm in good order because of restrictions on fertiliser and machinery, and the loss of manpower for war service.

Livestock on the holding included more than 20 horses, some working and others for breeding. In addition to having pigs, the family took over a flock of turkeys, an enterprise which was not renewed after the Christmas trade in that first year. As on most East Anglian farms of that period, bullocks were fattened in winter having been bought in as Irish stores.

There were 80 acres of grass and quite a bit of red clover, mown for hay and left for seed later. Because of the clover and pasture, fewer cereals were grown. The main arable crops were sugar beet and the appropriate quota of potatoes. Some fields were so derelict that they were difficult to get into production during the early years of World War Two.

Stephen remembers vividly that in the autumn of 1940, they were threshing corn when the threshing tackle caught alight and burned out. 'It was an absolute disaster because we couldn't buy any more threshing drums,' said Stephen. They had to wait for contractors, and when they had done their work the crop was taken to the old established firm of C.W. Byford & Sons at the nearby village of Clare. 'Mr Byford told us prices were up to 190 shillings a quarter – an enormous price at the time.' So Stephen's father agreed to sell the grain.

In those days Mr Byford would take the 6am train to Mark Lane (the main London grain market), arriving there at 7.30am. When he had completed his business, he returned to Suffolk on the 1pm train from Liverpool Street Station, arriving back at his office by 3pm. At 3.30pm, when on this particular day there had been no phone call from Mr Byford, Stephen was asked to find out whether he had got the price that had been suggested. 'No, I didn't,' Byford teased. 'I got 320 shillings a quarter.'

'That worked out at £60 or £70 a ton at a time when barley was selling for only £14 or £15 a ton,' said Stephen. 'It was the spirit of 1940, when the troops had come back from Dunkirk. There was no barley left, the country was in a mess and the men needed beer. Buyers were prepared to pay any amount just to get the barley.'

Stephen and his father would have been quite happy with 190 shillings a quarter, so they went to see Mr Byford to thank him personally. He looked at them in astonishment and asked what they were thanking him for. 'For getting the extra money,' they replied. 'Well, of course, I take half-a-crown a quarter, that's my commission – and anything else I get is for you,' the generous-hearted Mr Byford told them.

'This is the sort of thing that couldn't happen today,' Stephen Wise said. 'Firstly, there are no firms like that left; in fact, no large firm would allow that to happen.' However, their benefactor reaped the benefit through exclusive custom after that, and Mr Byford's grandson now has the neighbouring farm.

Stephen went to Leeds University for three years having wanted to go into the Army, but his father insisted that he came home, as farming was a reserved occupation. Farming was a hard life then, and not so appealing. The Wise family had 30 people working for them during the summer, clearing thistles and other weeds, then harvesting corn, sugar beet and potatoes. Stephen was thrown into work at the deep end and with the women who, he confides, were 'incredibly tough' and ready to make mincemeat of someone straight out of college.

Eugene Wise, who died in 1954, was recognised as one of the region's most progressive farmers, being one of the first to use pest control on the farm. He passed on much of his business acumen to his son, who took his father's advice and purchased his own sprayer. That immediately attracted the attention of neighbouring farmers, and they asked Eugene to 'send the boy' to do some spraying for them as well.

Stephen as the young entrepreneur.

'I had a hell of a good time going round the farm, talking to farmers and seeing their daughters,' Stephen laughed. Agreements were reached to pay him 2s 6d an acre for the work, and that added up to quite a sum at the end of the season. The young and still very enthusiastic Stephen Wise then seized the opportunity to set up his own spraying company – not a one-man band but a proper limited company. He went into business by forming the Agricultural Spraying Company with friend and neighbouring Cavendish farmer Basil Ambrose, himself a graduate of Newcastle University and later to be famed for his Cavendish Manor wine, a winner of major awards. The two men agreed to continue to farm their own land at the same time.

The partnership worked extremely well, having no competition whatsoever in its early days – 'a licence to print money,' was how Stephen described it. But like all boom times it was not destined to last. A number of competitors inevitably jumped on the bandwagon, and local garages in particular started to stock farm chemicals. As co-directors, Stephen and Basil decided not to join the commercial rat-race but to look ahead instead. They agreed that 'good, bad or indifferent, whatever happens in the United States of America, sooner or later happens in Britain.'

Stephen decided to take a 'busman's holiday' across the Atlantic, combining a bit of sightseeing with a look at what was happening in agriculture over there. He thought the trip should be arranged properly, so he contacted the United States Agricultural Attaché in London, a Mr Englund, and invited him to lunch at the Farmers' Club in London.

It took Mr Englund some weeks to organise, but an extensive itinerary

*Stephen Wise and his
late wife, Mary.*

was to take Stephen Wise to many states from the east coast to the west.
Further valuable help was given to him by the office of the US Secretary
for Agriculture on his arrival in America. Stephen repaid the generous
hospitality wherever he went by giving talks on British agriculture.

It was while on a holiday flight to Mexico City that Stephen met his
wife-to-be Mary, with whom he shared a taxi from the airport into the
city. They eventually married after a courtship which required lengthy
and frequent voyages across the Atlantic on some of the great ocean liners
of the day.

Back home after his first visit to America, Stephen revealed his
conclusions to his business partner: the next big development in
agriculture would be the mechanisation of livestock farming. But Basil
Ambrose didn't believe him, and went to America on a Nuffield
scholarship to see for himself. When he returned, he had to admit that
Stephen was right. The two men went to their accountant and said they
wanted to buy a whole or even half a company that had import and
export facilities – a manufacturing company – and, importantly, would
take livestock mechanisation in its stride. The accountant came up with
the name of J. Colman, so they bought the company, with John Colman
retaining a managing interest. At first they were based in London, but
transferred the works nearer home to Sudbury. The name remained as
Colman & Company from 1960 to 1976, when Stephen and Basil sold
out. John Colman stayed on as managing director with the new company.

Stephen went back to his farm and also became involved with a

number of organisations. He represented Suffolk as a council delegate of
the Contractors Association, while owning the spraying company, and
became one of the few people who have twice served as chairman of the
Sudbury branch of the National Farmers' Union. He is also a Liveryman
of the prestigious Worshipful Company of Farmers. Stephen also served
as chairman of the House Committee of the Sue Ryder Home in
Cavendish, and was a founder member of Amnesty International in
Suffolk, serving as treasurer and secretary at various times.

Three periods of English history in the building of Houghton Hall

There is an undulating drive from the main road along a rough track (in
need of planned redevelopment work to bring it up to standard), exactly
two-thirds of a mile long, to reach Houghton Hall, a remote manor house
with 500 acres of farm land and a large percentage of original moat. The
property lies on the edge of the picturesque village of Cavendish, near
Sudbury.

Try viewing this large, Grade II listed house front and rear while
walking in its ample gardens and you will be lured into the erroneous
conclusion that you cannot be looking at the same building. This is
because its architecture bears witness to three ages of English history.
Owner Stephen Wise says there was a dwelling on the site recorded in the

The Georgian front of Houghton Hall, Cavendish.

*Another view of the
Georgian front of
Houghton Hall,
Cavendish.*

Domesday Book of 1086, and he best explains the unusual appearance of
the present manor house.

Stephen's father, Eugene, a progressive Central European farmer from
a family of farmers going back well into the early 19th century, bought
the manor house when he came to England with his family in the late
1930s. He wanted an arable farm, the stipulation for purchase being that
it should be in a ring fence, with plenty of cottages for his workers and a
good farmhouse. Houghton Hall met these criteria.

Stephen believes that building work took place in stages over centuries.
'The back of the house came first because of the way the roof is
constructed,' he told me. 'As you come further south, the middle of house
is of the Tudor period. We know it is Tudor because the dining room has
ceiling beams of a special shape.

'I was chairman of the house committee of the Sue Ryder charity, at a
time when Sue was given a lot of old houses to make into homes for the
charity's permanent residents. She engaged the kind of architect who
specialised and, because it was work for a charity, gave his services free.

'One day, after a meeting in Cavendish, I invited the architect to
accompany me to Houghton Hall for a cup of tea. He examined the huge
ceiling timbers and declared that they were ship's timbers from King
Henry VIII's navy. The ships had been laid up and eventually, as nothing
was wasted in those days, they were used in home construction. The
timbers therefore verified that the centre of the house was constructed in
the 16th century.'

The typical Georgian front of the house dates from 1854. Stephen knows the exact date because a man who came to tea in the early 1950s said that his grandmother had lived in the house, and her records showed when the Georgian front was put on.

The mediaeval rear of Houghton Hall. The centre of the hall is of Tudor origin.

Houghton Hall has a very good cellar which maintains a constant temperature that fluctuates by no more than five degrees up or down. Wine keeps so well that some bottles he bought for 12 shillings and six pence in the 1950s were sold at Christies in the mid-1980s for £150 a bottle. Said Stephen: 'The moat is also historical, it was here in mediaeval times. I'm told it was for keeping fish in winter. The moat used to go nearly all the way round, now it is about 50 percent.'

Talented family benefit from being in the right place at the right time

The close Anglo-American ties which began in the courtship days of Stephen and Mary Wise have been passed on to their very talented family. Son Robert and elder daughter Eileen both have knowledge of the inner workings of government at the highest level, the former in the United States and the latter in Britain. Younger daughter Deborah is not only a high-profile journalist and author, but lives in Brazil with her journalist husband and family.

After education at Ampleforth College, Robert gained a BSc (Hons) degree in agriculture at Newcastle University, and with the advantage of having dual nationality and therefore two passports, went on to study for a Masters degree in agricultural economics at Michigan State University.

How Robert came to work in the offices of the White House was, according to his father, a case of 'being in the right place at the right time.' A professor at Michigan University, who had taken a liking to him, took a trip to Washington DC at about the time Robert was coming to the end of his degree course. The professor was asked by someone in the State Department if he knew of any bright young men who could be sent to Washington for interviews. He said he had two, one of whom was Robert. Later Robert, who was expected home after he finished university, phoned home instead with surprise news for his parents. 'Guess what?' he said, 'I've got a job in government.' 'Oh, yes. Where?' replied Stephen. 'The White House,' came the reply.

Robert stayed on in America with the full approval of his father, who believed it was not only important to be in the right place at the right time, but to do the right thing. Robert was later to meet future wife Leslie Berger, who at that time was working in the United States Department of Agriculture. After his stint at the White House, he got a job as an agricultural economic adviser with Tom Daschle, then a 'junior' senator from South Dakota. Now, 20 years later, Senator Daschle is Senate Minority Leader.

One day, Leslie was called into her office and told she was being transferred to the diplomatic service arising from service in the Peace Corps in Africa for two years – and to her surprise was further told that her posting would be in London. So Robert gave up his job and returned to England as a diplomat's husband. Six months later Robert got a job with the UK grain and feed organisation UKASTA in London. Leslie was given an eminent appointment as Agricultural Attaché at the United States Embassy with her own steward to escort her to many events, including the Suffolk Show and the Royal Show in Warwickshire.

After three years of high office, Leslie was asked to return to Washington, but by now she and Robert were settled in Britain, so she resigned to enable them to continue living in England. They now live in Cavendish and have two children. Although the farm land at Houghton Hall has been contract farmed since Stephen's retirement, Robert remains responsible for its organisation and book work, and operates his own consultancy. Stephen said life could be 'very strange,' pointing out that the first American he met officially at the London Embassy in 1955 was the Agricultural Attaché, the same post held by Leslie, his daughter-in-law, 35 years later.

Stephen described his elder daughter, Eileen, as being 'a big fish in a big pond' in public relations and journalism. In PR, she worked for a number of eminent companies, including the Walt Disney organisation, Andrew Lloyd Webber and Selfridges. At the time she joined the Robert Maxwell organisation for a period of only nine weeks, he was launching *The European* newspaper. Before leaving, Maxwell told her she was a remarkable woman. 'Why?' she asked, 'Because you have been here nine weeks, and I couldn't make you cry,' was the reply. Such was the man's vile reputation with his staff.

Probably Eileen's most high-profile appointment was as head of news at the Conservative Party office in Smith Square, when she was very active during the latter days of John Major's tenancy of 10 Downing Street. She also worked in public relations in the United States for two years.

As a journalist, Eileen worked for *Hello!* magazine, the Ross Benson column in the *Daily Express*, and the equivalent column in the *Daily Mail*. She is now public relations manager for *The Economist* weekly magazine.

Stephen's younger daughter, Deborah, earned a reputation as a high-flying journalist on both sides of the Atlantic. She finished school in England as head girl of sport at Newhouse School, Chelmsford, and went on to gain an Honours degree at Boston University. The reason she went to the United States was because there was a rule in those days that no-one could retain American citizenship unless they were in residence for three years. After university, Deborah was a staff writer on the American *Business Week* magazine, later being transferred from New York to the San Francisco office. On her return home she became a staff writer for *The Guardian* and also wrote occasional articles for the *New York Times*.

Although by now an established journalist, Deborah told her father that she preferred not to remain a journalist all her life, but wanted to be an author. During an 18-month period in Paris, she made one of her periodic visits to America, where at a party she met a Frenchman who offered her work writing a book on the world-famous French flautist, Jean Pierre Rampal. Yet again, said Stephen, it was a case of being in the right place at the right time. Deborah returned to Paris to spend nine months writing an autobiography which carried the accreditation 'By Jean Pierre Rampal, as told to Deborah Wise.' Rampal died in 2002, aged 78.

Deborah met and later married journalist Brook Unger, who became a chief correspondent on *The Economist*. Brook was later assigned to overseas duties in Berlin and New Delhi. And after three years covering events in India, he was transferred for a further three years to São Paulo, the commercial centre of Brazil, where he lives with Deborah and their two children.

Cavendish – home of the famous centuries ago and modern times

The village of Cavendish has played its part in British history. In 1381 during the Peasants Revolt, Sir John Cavendish hung on to the handle of the church door for sanctuary from his pursuers. It is therefore amazing that the same handle still hangs on the door more than six centuries later.

The village is also known for its association with the Devonshires and the Colts, two of the great English families. It was also the home of the late Sue Ryder (later created Baroness Ryder of Warsaw, the title she chose because of the help she gave to Polish people during and after World War Two). The wife of war hero Group Captain Leonard Cheshire VC, and founder of the national foundation that bears her name, Margaret Susan Ryder was the youngest of nine children, and her father was a farmer. The Sue Ryder Foundation Museum in Cavendish was opened by the Queen Mother in 1979, but the last years of Lady Ryder's life were dogged by ill health, and there were also wrangles with her foundation committee shortly before her recent death.

Because of the village's comparative importance through the ages, Cavendish has five manors. Others include Nether Hall and Colts Hall. Nether Hall, a two-storey, timber-framed farmhouse, is the home of Stephen Wise's friend and former business partner, Basil Ambrose, who until he retired a few years ago, was the producer of the noted Cavendish Manor wine from the vineyards he planted in 1972. The windows of the manor house were originally mullioned.

Colts Hall, the home of John Wayman and his wife Adele, who are also friends of Stephen Wise, is on farm land situated 300ft above sea level – a fairly high point for Suffolk – and its occupants often feel the cutting edge of winter winds whistling in from Siberia. However, the farmhouse was built to stand the test of time and the harshest elements, its oldest timbers dating back to 1330. In 1985, the Haverhill archaeological group carried out a dig on the back meadow of Colts Hall and unearthed 'bits and pieces' of pottery of the 14th and 15th century.

The house name Colt is derived from the Colt family who owned the property in the 15th century. Jane, the sister of Sir George Colt, was the first wife of Sir Thomas More. The house and farm remained in the ownership of the Colt family until the late 18th century, when it became the property of the later titled Earl Howe. Charles Ray bought the farm in 1917, making only the third family to have ownership in some 500 years.

When Charles Ray died in 1932, he left virtually everything to his only nephew, John Wayman's father. The 1,200 acres of land that came into the Wayman family at that time were divided into four farms: two in Essex, at Belchamp St Paul, which were owned; Hill Farm, Clare, where he was a tenant of the Clare Priory Estate, and Colts Hall. Because John's father wished to continue as a practising solicitor, he employed a farm manager, and from 1939 took on John Garrett, who stayed with the family until 1970.

John Wayman, who was later to become Mayor of Bury St Edmunds, having represented Cavendish on St Edmundsbury Council for a number of years, studied at the Royal Agricultural College at Cirencester in the early 1960s and took over the farming operations on John Garrett's retirement. John and Adele have possession of a copy of the *East Anglian Daily Times* dated 12 June 1891. The edition, which is remarkably preserved after more than a century of careful storage, contains a report of the marriage of John's grandfather, Francis Wayman, to Alice Ray.

John Wayman is the current chairman of the South Suffolk Agricultural Association's annual crop competition… a fact that leads on to the final chapter in the Stephen Wise story.

Half a century as secretary of Britain's top crop competition

My wife and I have attended the South Suffolk Agricultural Association's annual crop competition dinner and prize giving for all but one of the last 34 years, at the kind invitation of Stephen Wise and the organising committee. The only time we have missed the event was because of illness, and on another memorable occasion it was an honour to be invited as guest speaker.

Stephen was for half a century the secretary of one of the largest competitions of its kind in the country, acting as principal organiser until his retirement from the office in the autumn of 2003.

For most of the 40-50 participants each year, the autumn trophy presentation evening is a permanent entry in the year's social calendar –

one not to be missed by some 100–150 people. For me it has always been a joy to see the hard-working farmers of south Suffolk and, in some cases, members of their farm staff, relaxed and enjoying themselves away from the fields.

Stephen recalls that he was appointed secretary when the competition first began simply because he was the youngest member of the committee. By the time he completed his mission in 2003, at the age of 81, all the other members of the original committee were dead.

The beginnings of the competition can be traced back to the neglected state of agriculture before World War Two. It was during the war years, when the need to increase food production was essential to Britain's survival, that the Government, through its 'Dig for Victory' campaign, began to educate farmers by encouraging the formation of local committees and discussion groups.

When the Long Melford discussion group became defunct after the war, the question arose of what to do with funds of two or three hundred pounds – a large sum in those days. It was finally decided to donate the money to the South Suffolk Agricultural Society, which ran an annual one-day show. However, it was also necessary to find another use for the cash. Stephen, who was then successfully breeding pigs, was elected on to the committee.

The committee chairman was Arthur Cobbald, of Acton Hall, who came back from judging a farms competition in the West Country with a solution to the problem – they would have a crop competition. That was in 1953, and the first competition was held the following year. There have been six chairmen since then, the latest being friend and neighbour John Wayman, of Colts Hall. Stephen has always been content to be secretary, stating that he got nothing but enjoyment from the enormous amount of work it involved.

The competition has evolved over the years and adapted to reflect the changing patterns of agricultural production. It began with eight classes – two each for wheat, barley, oats and sugar beet – and now has 18. For example, Suffolk being a big wheat growing county, the wheat classes are subdivided into bread-making and biscuit-making varieties, over and under 40 years, to make the logistics manageable. Varieties, of course, have changed so that the popular ones of the past are outclassed and unknown to some of the younger competitors.

Yields have also advanced, but the biggest change has perhaps been the increase in the size of participating farms. Whereas there used to be classes of 250 acres, under and over 500 acres, there is no longer a class for 250 acres. Nowadays there are four categories, from 400 to 1,000 acres. Each of the acreage classes has a championship, and the supreme championship goes to the one with the most points.

Some 250 fields are entered each year, but farmers drawn from a restricted area of a 13-mile radius of Cavendish are fewer in number. However, some farmers taking part are from much further away because they were first accepted before the 13-mile rule came in. Family influence has been responsible for several generations being involved in the event.

Judges serve two years and come from the surrounding counties of Essex, Cambridgeshire, Norfolk and Lincolnshire, and also from east Suffolk if they are not too close. Their route for judging the standing crops, which takes place in June and July, is worked out by the steward.

A considerable amount of valuable silverware – the 20 cups are now valued at £12,000 – is distributed at the annual dinner, which has always attracted a 'full house.' I began attending as soon as I joined the *EADT* editorial team in 1969, and proceedings after the meal have always taken roughly the same format: an introduction by the competition chairman, followed by an address by the guest speaker, who then leads the presentation of trophies and a generous number of prize certificates. Judges also present awards for their own categories.

There have been four venues for the 49 presentation evenings to 2003. The first dinners were held at Sudbury Town Hall, but when numbers outgrew the venue, the event was moved to the Athenaeum at Bury St Edmunds. It was there for many years, but because acoustics were so bad the venue was changed to Bury's Corn Exchange. A further change was made a few years ago and the event is now held in the excellent hotel with parking facilities at the Stoke by Nayland Golf Club.

Running the competition secretariat has been hard though enjoyable work for Stephen Wise, but he did have the pleasure of winning the supreme championship himself some 20 years ago.

CHAPTER 7

Glemham Hall, Little Glemham

Glemham Hall, a brick-built mansion of the Elizabethan period, was built in around 1560, about 200 yards from the site of an earlier moated manor or hall which belonged to the Glemhams, a family which took its name from its location, Great (Magna) and Little (Parva) Glemham, near Saxmundham. Rye's 'Calendar of the Feet of Fines for Suffolk' contains several references to the family, the earliest being William de Glemham relating to the property at Glemham in 1228–29.

The Glemhams prospered under the Tudors, and there is evidence that Princess Mary Tudor, dowager Queen of France whose second marriage was to Charles Brandon, Duke of Suffolk, made occasional visits to Sir

Glemham Hall.

John Glemham at the former hall, during a long stay at Butley Priory in 1527.

The Glemham family branched off to the neighbouring manor of Benhall, which was the property for a time of one of its most colourful members – an Elizabethan sea-dog, Edward Glemham – in an age when adventures against the Spaniards were more akin to piracy than orthodox warfare. Edward's voyages brought him the kind of renown enjoyed by his contemporaries, Drake and Raleigh. His exploits were recorded in a pamphlet published in 1651 which had the lengthy title: *The Honourable Actions of that most famous and valiant Englishman Edward Glemham Esquire, latelie obtained against the Spaniards and the Holy League in four sundre fightes.*

Edward's buccaneering may have brought him lustre but did not improve his financial position. Although he was recorded as at first being 'a man of substance feasting his friends and relieving the poor plentifully,' his fortunes declined and he had to sell Benhall.

Meanwhile, his cousin and neighbour, Sir Henry Glemham, was flourishing, and it was he who originally created the new Glemham Hall and made it such a beautiful example of the Early Renaissance style with its gatehouse, pavilions and enclosing walls. Sir Henry married Anne Sackville, a daughter of Thomas Sackville, Earl of Dorset and Lord High Treasurer. He was succeeded by his son Sir Thomas, who was an MP for Aldeburgh, and who subsequently won a reputation as a stubborn fighter for Charles I in the Civil War. Sir Thomas was Governor of York, and when forced to surrender to the Roundheads, he and a Yorkshire Cavalier, Sir Henry Slingsby, marched out with their regiments to continue their efforts in Lancashire and Cumberland. There they parted, Glemham holding out bravely at Carlisle and only giving it up after, it is alleged, his soldiers had been forced to eat their own horses (Sir Thomas was also said to be the first man to teach hungry soldiers to eat cats and dogs). From Carlisle, which he left with the honours of war, he went to South Wales to join the King and then took command at Oxford. In 1648 he was fighting in Scotland but died soon afterwards, for in 1650 his brother Henry, Bishop of St Asaph, is on record as proving his will.

The history of Glemham Hall – indeed of Little Glemham itself – during the second half of the 17th century is rather obscure, probably because the parish registers from 1658 to 1748 are said to have been destroyed by the parish clerk 'in a fit of insanity.' According to manuscripts deposited in the Archives Office of Kent County Council at

Maidstone by the Earl of Guilford, a descendant of the North family who later owned Glemham Hall, the Glemhams did not sell the estate until 1708 or 1709. The purchaser from Thomas Glemham (a grandson of the Cavalier) was Dudley North, son of Sir Dudley North, a well-known merchant and grandson of Dudley, the 4th Baron North. An account book belonging to Dudley North shows that in March 1708, £15,000 was allotted for the purchase of the estate, including the repayment of the principal sum and interest on all four mortgages.

On 14 April 1709, a further £620 was paid to Thomas Glemham for small additional purchases at the time the deeds were signed. Dudley's wife, Catherine, was a daughter of Elihu Yale, founder of the famous American university. Yale was born in the United States but when he was four years old his parents returned to Britain. When he grew up, he entered the service of the East India Company and was one of the many

The Cobbolds of Glemham Hall family tree.

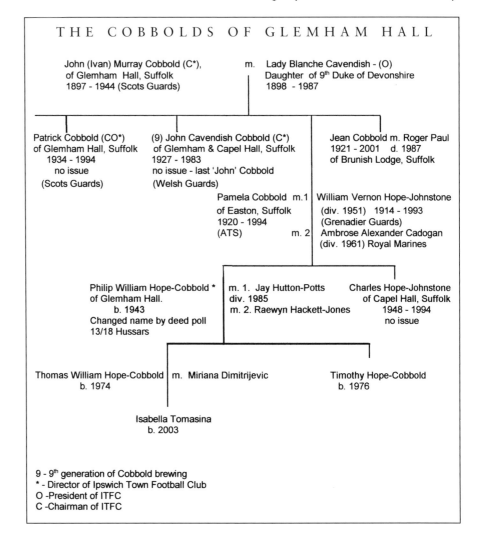

acquisitive Governors of Madras who got into trouble because of private trading – but only after amassing fortunes for themselves.

Generous with the wealth he accumulated, Elihu Yale endowed the university and was also lavish in his gifts to his family, including his daughter and co-heir, Dudley North's wife. Glemham Hall obtained many treasures at this time as a result. Unfortunately, Catherine died in 1715, only a few years after her husband had purchased the property.

Considerable structural changes were made to the Hall between 1712 and 1722 (the date is still to be found on the rainwater heads) and so far as the exterior is concerned, they can hardly be considered improvements, for with them disappeared many graceful Elizabethan features. The main entrance was given a Palladian flavour and the attractive gabled attic storey was raised up in brickwork to entirely hide the roof, thus giving the front of the house a rather austere appearance. The porch and bays were removed and long lines of sash windows were inserted.

One feature of the Elizabethan elevation was retained: the tower section of the pair of stone pilasters which had been placed between the mullioned windows and had been balanced by similar ones at the porch corners. Inside the older hall was retained but the screen was replaced by four fluted Corinthian columns and the walls wainscoted with the large panels then in vogue and painted white.

Glemham Hall remained in various branches of the North family for more than 200 years. Sir Dudley's male line ended with his grandson in 1764. This grandson, another Dudley North, and his sister both married children of the Earl of Pembroke and at his death, his sister, the Hon. Mrs Herbert, succeeded him. She outlived her children and when she died in 1789 she left the estate to her younger sister's son, Dudley Long. He died childless in 1819.

After that Glemham reverted to the Norths and became the property of the 8th Earl of Guilford. For some time it was the home of his grandmother, Lady North, who lived there with her eldest son, Eden Dickson. During World War One the Hall was let to a member of the Cunard family. In 1923 Glemham Hall was purchased by the Cobbold family.

Brewing, farming and football – the main interests of the Cobbolds

The first of the Cobbold brewing family to occupy Glemham Hall was Captain John (Ivan) Murray Cobbold – the first chairman of Ipswich

Town Football Club after it turned professional in 1936 – and his wife, Lady Blanche, a daughter of the 9th Duke of Devonshire and his wife, Evelyn, a daughter of the Marquess of Landsdowne. Captain Cobbold – by then Colonel – was killed in 1944 when the Guards Chapel in London was destroyed by a flying bomb.

The Cobbold family were originally yeoman farmers around Tostock and Rattlesden before new brewing wealth enabled them to acquire the Holywells Estate in Ipswich (now Holywells Park), leaving there when they took over at Glemham Hall in 1923 at a time when Ipswich began expanding.

Lady Blanche lived in the Hall until her death on 16 October 1987 – a significant date in the history of East Anglia – the day of what became

Aerial view of Glemham Hall and the surrounding estate.

known as the great storm, which brought about the destruction of millions of trees throughout the region. It is believed that Lady Blanche was so shocked when she saw from her bedroom window the destruction and damage to some of the ancient trees on the estate's parkland that she suffered a minor heart attack that morning and a fatal one later the same day. Glemham was handed over to her younger son, Patrick, who lived at the hall and ran the estate.

The present incumbent is former army major Philip Hope-Cobbold, who inherited the estate in January 1995, following the death of his revered uncle, Patrick, who had also been chairman of Ipswich Town FC. Like his recent ancestors, Philip has always had a great interest in football, even though he was quite often stationed many miles away from Suffolk. He was invited to join the Ipswich Town board of directors in 1995, and thus continues the family connection with the football club.

To the manor born

It was in 1943 that Philip became the first of only two members of the Cobbold family to actually be born at the Hall. 'I have come home to roost,' he laughed when I met him for the first time in April 1997, a memorable occasion for me.

Philip was educated at Kings College Choir School, Radley College and the Royal Military Academy Sandhurst, from where he was commissioned in 1964 into the 13th/18th Royal Hussars (Queen Mary's Own), serving with the regiment until 1992, including postings to Germany, Canada, Northern Ireland, Oman and at home in the Ministry of Defence. His return to Suffolk to take over the running of the Glemham Hall Estate came two years after finishing a military career of some 29 years and nine months.

Some changes in the running of the Glemham Hall Estate

'I love it here. It's an oasis of a place to live on, a very beautiful place. Just less than 3,000 acres is a handy area to be able to look after, and the 200–250 acres of park around the house are a wonderful piece of countryside with all the ancient trees in it' – these were the words of Philip Hope-Cobbold when I revisited the Glemham Hall Estate in December 2003, after a gap of more than six years.

I was very late for the appointment, because accidents had caused huge

*The grand staircase
and servants' livery at
Glemham Hall.*
Graham Portlock

traffic jams and long delays in Ipswich, where I live, and I had to travel many miles out of my way, finally cutting across country to Little Glemham. I sat in the car fuming, but the delay gave plenty of time to recall my first, memorable visit to the Hall in April 1997.

Philip had then been resident on the estate for only two years after leaving the Army, when I telephoned for an appointment on a sunny April morning. He agreed to meet me that same day, and the visit was to prove quite an adventure. The great house is an imposing sight from a winding stretch of the A12, and as I entered the grounds I was, on that occasion, seeing Glemham Hall at the best time of year, with thousands of daffodils in bloom lining the driveway to the house.

After a talk inside the Hall, I was invited to ride 'pillion passenger' on his quad bike, clinging on for dear life as we set off on a tour of the estate, with the family's Labrador running alongside. It was a glorious afternoon on All Fools Day, and responding to Philip's call of 'All aboard!', it was too late to be considered 'chicken,' or even to heed the warning of someone who enquired whether I was insured to risk life and limb. The short journey was fun, if a little scary, as we bounced along across the farmland's rough terrain on the wide-tyred vehicle, and I admit to being relieved when we changed to a more conventional form of transport for the remaining part of the conducted tour.

My request for a return visit to Glemham Hall was met with an equally swift and positive response from Philip. We chatted at the annual meeting of the Suffolk Agricultural Association, and after a quick look at his crowded diary, he agreed to a visit the following morning. There was no daffodil welcome this time, of course, but a warm handshake from my genial host, and after another chat indoors, we walked out to see work being carried out in the rose and autumn gardens to prepare for public visits and events during the following year.

The walled rose garden was in the process of being completely revamped under the supervision of Philip's wife, Raewyn, in an effort to open it to the public more often. Raewyn, a New Zealander, has lived in Britain for some 30 years, and at the time I met her, the couple were approaching their first wedding anniversary.

More than 400 new roses, provided by David Austin of Wolverhampton, under a helpful sponsorship agreement, were about to be planted in 400 tonnes of a new soil mixture already in the ground. New attractions to help the estate's growing commercial interests include a permanent marquee with seating for 200 guests, which is well hidden in

the garden behind hedges and between walls – 'It is out of sight except from the air,' said Philip. 'We hope to develop facilities more so that we can have any sort of event here.' Several musical events have been held in the house and gardens in recent years. The aim is to increase the use of the marquee for corporate entertainment and other events in order to generate income to help with the costly overall maintenance of such a large house as the 67-room Glemham Hall. Historical events – possibly Elizabethan – are also a possibility in the future. When Philip's stepson, William Hackett-Jones, was married at the hall in July 2003, he chose a mediaeval themed wedding. The house is licensed for civil marriage ceremonies, renewal of marriage vows and naming ceremonies. These are held in the hall, with receptions in the garden on a summer's day, or in the marquee. In addition to the walled rose garden, a summer house, a lily pond and classical urns, the gardens display traditional English symmetry. The wide lawns and garden are framed by yew hedges and surrounded by the parkland.

Regular events include the Suffolk Game and Country Fair during the May Bank Holiday weekend, and in 2003 there was a visit by the Ancient Tree Forum, who delighted in the oak trees in the park. 'They told me they were exceptional, and they also told me I have to look after them, which I do as best I can,' said Philip.

In fact, there has been a considerable replanting in recent years. A lot of well-established trees were lost in the woods during the Great Storm of October 1987, and old age also got to some of those in the park, so there is now an ongoing planting programme of oaks, ash and other native trees, including some new lime trees at the rear of the house to add to those that have been carefully nurtured over many years.

The maintenance of Glemham Hall, as with other stately homes, is a constant headache and expense. The next big job is repair of the final part of the roof, and Philip is hoping that English Heritage will provide a grant towards the cost in the near future, as work is needed urgently to repair some roof leaks on the west side of the building. 'Everything needs maintenance, it's like the Forth Bridge,' he laughed.

There have been several prestigious additions inside the building to commemorate the millennium. A large round table was made by craftsmen of the Ipswich firm of Titchmarsh and Goodwin. Oak and ash from the estate were used in this special millennium project, and below the table top is a time capsule, made from the wood of felled oak from the royal Sandringham estate, when the makers ran out of Glemham oak

The nursery in April 1999. Graham Portlock

after they had also made Philip a four-poster bed for upstairs. Philip would not say what was in the capsule, but opined that, in theory, it should not be opened for 1,000 years. Other welcome additions to the contents of the Hall are some Mendlesham chairs made by another craftsman, Albert Lane, who works from his farm and house at Peasenhall, and on the wall is a large oil painting of the rose garden by local artist Tim Fargher, of Orford.

A few changes had taken place since my last visit with regard to the management of the farm estate. Although former agent Tony Flick has retired, the agency work is carried on by Flick and Son. Richard Leaming is now the agent, continuing where Tony left off. The farm land is now contract farmed by a well-known Suffolk farming family, John Kerr and his sons. The farming area is much the same and the estate also has the same tenants: Roger Blyth, Martin Greenfield and John Kerr. The light land on the east of the estate's farm land now grows onions, carrots and potatoes.

'A lot of people who come here like seeing the cattle,' said Philip. 'We don't have our own suckler herd anymore, we now have beef cattle from March to October or November; then the park is left to rest and

The beautiful millennium table inside the Great Hall at Glemham Hall, made from oak and ash trees grown on the estate. Inset: The wooden time capsule – not be be opened for another 1,000 years – can be seen in the centre of the base.

recuperate before we start fattening cattle again the following year. We also have a lot of deer – mainly fallow and muntjac – and they are becoming quite a problem. We have a few red deer, which stray out from the coastal area around Dunwich. We don't capture them, but we have to cull them selectively to keep the numbers down, otherwise all the effort that goes into replanting new hedgerows and trees is for nothing. Roe deer are also a problem, particularly if you are replanting new hedgerows; they tend to nibble the lot if you let them. Not that we want to get rid of them, of course. It's nice to have healthy stock, but it's like all these things, if the balance goes too far one way it can be a problem, not only for us but also for people with gardens when the deer get in. We simply need a balance. It's lovely to have them, but...'

One decision reluctantly taken, especially as his grandmother, Lady Blanche Cobbold had brought them with her from Chatsworth shortly after her marriage, was to dispense with the Jacob sheep flock, which was one of the oldest in the country of the breed. In economic terms, 'it was very difficult to justify keeping them on,' Philip said.

Pipps Ford – a small country hotel run by Raewyn Hope-Cobbold

Raewyn, Philip Hope-Cobbold's New Zealand-born wife, runs a separate small private hotel business known as Pipps Ford, a 16th-century farmhouse set in a beautiful stretch of the River Gipping, near Needham Market. The Manor of Pipps is said to have been given to Richard Hakluyt, the 16th-century explorer. The house is situated on the site of Stone Age battles, close to the Romano-British settlement of Combretovium.

Pipps Ford stands in a delightful old-fashioned garden, surrounded by farmland and meadows. Both hotel and its proprietor have won a number of prestigious awards, including RAC winner of Small Hotel for the Eastern Region, and Raewyn was a finalist for Landlady of the Year. The hotel was also featured in ITV's *Wish You Were Here* programme with Judith Chalmers, and Elizabeth Gundrey's *Staying off the Beaten Track*. There are some eight rooms offering accommodation.

Pipps Ford is also available for events such as house parties, celebratory dinners and lunch parties, christenings and small weddings, business meetings and breakfasts and small conferences.

CHAPTER 8

Gedgrave Hall, Orford

It is the moment that you pass the 12th-century Orford Castle, on the way, via a narrow back road, to Gedgrave, that you are suddenly imbued with a sense of history and wonder, for the castle is such an imposing monument to mediaeval England. You know then that you are only minutes away from Gedgrave Hall, which on a dank day in early January seems a bleak outpost of coastal Suffolk.

I never made it to the house, for in my hesitation about its location, having been there only once before several years before, I stopped my car at the side of the road and was passed by another, driven by host Sir Edward Greenwell, who motioned me to follow. He led me to his farm office, almost opposite the hall.

On my previous visit to Gedgrave in the mid-1990s, I was given a roller-coaster ride across fields to the high bank which separates the marsh grazing land from the River Ore and, further east, Orfordness and the sea. The short journey had a purpose other than to provide me with a photo opportunity: Sir Edward wanted to change a light bulb on top of his half-submerged drainage pump, so that he could see it from his bedroom window half a mile away and know that the pump was operating properly. Nearby Orfordness has its own place in British history with the establishment of the first experimental radar station on the coastal site in 1935.

Sir Edward's grandfather, Sir Bernard Greenwell, Bt, bought the Gedgrave Hall farm estate along with various other farms in the 1930s. The Gedgrave land had been part of the Sudbourne Hall Estate, which was starting to be broken up for sale in 1918 and was subsequently sold and re-sold several times during the 1920s. So what had originally been 11,000 acres was divided more and more, and this was happening simultaneously with the next large estate inland, the Rendlesham Hall Estate, which had once covered 20,000 acres and ran roughly from the A12 road to Butley Creek. 'Now that, too, is in many different ownerships,' said Sir Edward. 'My grandfather was buying land in Suffolk because he had an estate in Surrey. He worked in London and when he heard that land was for sale in Suffolk for £5 per acre, he felt this had to be good value.'

Sir Bernard died in 1939, and his grandson doubts whether he would have seen any return at all because, he said, it was the war that put agriculture back on its feet, 'and agricultural policy since, at least until now, has roughly kept it there.'

Sir Edward Greenwell on his Gedgrave Hall Estate, near Orford.

The Greenwell family originates from Durham, where they had a 190-acre hill farm called Greenwell, the family ownership of which dates back to at least 1183. The farm is still owned by them. The property, which has a small stone farmhouse, stone farmyard and modern buildings added over time, has been farmed by tenants from the same family for well over a century.

Before World War Two, the family estate in east Suffolk extended to some 7,000 acres, but Sir Edward's father, Sir Peter, sold some of the land in the early 1950s because he could not afford to farm it at that time. However, shortly afterwards he bought some more land at Tunstall, a small let estate, which over the years has lost all but one of its tenant farmers. The Herring family are now the only original tenants remaining, though there are other arrangements for farming the land.

The total area now under Greenwell family ownership is around 5,500 acres and is split between Sir Edward and his brother James. They farm side by side, sometimes sharing facilities and machinery, but as separate businesses.

Sir Edward suspects that Gedgrave Hall had been part of the Sudbourne Hall Estate for many hundreds of years, and tenanted out. With regard to the actual location of Gedgrave (which only appears on the largest maps), originally there was a church or chapel, shown on old maps of around the 16th century, 'and if you dig around between here [the office] and the house, there are quite a lot of bodies.'

No one is sure when the marshes were reclaimed, but Sir Edward believes it was achieved gradually, in compartments, and it would have been possible for sheep and cattle to graze the reclaimed areas, even as saltings. 'I imagine that in the Middle Ages, when the land was all owned by the Church, whether by Butley Abbey or Snape Priory, or indeed the church of St Edmund, the landowners would have taken bits of marshland and put low earth banks around them, so that they would have suffered fewer salt-water floodings. This would have improved the grazing, and this would have improved further over the centuries, starting, as far as we know, in the 14th century or possibly earlier.'

Gedgrave consists of some 1,100 acres, and about half of it is reclaimed land. Today the parish is part of Orford. Even before the East Coast Floods at the end of January 1953, arable crops were being grown on the reclaimed marsh at Gedgrave. After 1953, all sea defence walls were put in to a standard height which far surpassed what was there before and enabled people to invest in artificial drainage and electric pumps. No problems were experienced during the very high tides, almost 50 years later, in December 2003.

'Luckily, the Gedgrave walls are mostly made of clay, and sit on clay,' said Sir Edward. 'The walls are not quite as good as they were in the late fifties, but they haven't changed a lot. I haven't seen the tides within two feet of the top of them – yet.' However, he says he does not have confidence in the political will to maintain the sea defences. 'As an owner, I might be willing to maintain them, but I am not even permitted to do that unless I get planning permission, and unless English Nature does not object to that planning permission, which they almost certainly will because there is a desire to see nature take its course and the original pattern of the coastline re-establish itself.'

The farming at Gedgrave, certainly until the 1953 floods, would have centred on livestock. Most of the capital would have been in livestock and most of the turnover likewise. The arable ground would have been growing turnips or kale for dairy herds, and that continued from when the sea defence walls were built until about 1980, when the pressure of

cost of labour and the very low rainfall, and therefore low yields from grazing livestock and dairy cows in particular, made it impossible to continue. 'So we went out of dairy cows and out of beef animals, and it was only with the coming of the Environmentally Sensitive Area (ESA) schemes that livestock have come back to Gedgrave, and we have now got 200–250 acres of land back from arable into grass, mostly with sheep on, but some cattle, so the whole thing is reversing itself, slowly,' said Sir Edward. 'The arable land is grade four – blowing sand – and without irrigation water it would be hopeless. In fact, I doubt whether we would be farming that land at all without irrigation. Some land around here doesn't have irrigation and you see outdoor pigs followed by a couple of rye crops, then more outdoor pigs.'

The Greenwell brothers have adequate irrigation water, because their father invested in irrigation from about 1954 onwards, the first underground mains going in the following year. But even though the present water situation is satisfactory, Sir Edward believes there is a big question mark over future supplies because of a reassessment now being made about the balance between environment, agriculture and public water supply, which will be reviewed in the coming years. Ancient licences of right to take water have been abolished, he said.

Farming on coastal reclaimed land presents its own challenges.

'It is not guaranteed that we will have those water supplies, but it is, absolutely, the key to farming this land. With water on the sand land you can grow vegetables, you can grow potatoes and you can actually grow them rather well. They are quite intensive crops and it means that levels of employment are much higher than they would otherwise be. That's not true only of us but the whole of the sandlings, and without water the farming population would be a lot smaller, and a lot poorer.'

Sir Edward and Lady Sarah have three daughters and a son, Alec, who at 16 years of age does not yet know a lot about the running of a rural estate, but shows his love of the countryside. 'That's the first thing to instil in young people, that they really enjoy the countryside and want to be part of it in the future,' says Sir Edward. It's a similar situation for his brother, who has a daughter, and a son, aged 20, who is reading an agricultural subject at Newcastle University, but gets involved in the farming when at home. So they both have a new generation coming along to follow in their footsteps. Sir Edward's three daughters, Belinda, Lucy and Daisy also love the countryside. Two are at present working in London, and the third is at university.

On a final personal note, Sir Edward admits to feeling a little sad that that he is no longer farming directly. 'I went into contract farming in 1992 and although it does seem a more efficient way to run things, I do have regrets that I am not so closely linked to the land,' he said. 'The good thing about it is that it clarifies the management, i.e. what you are doing, what is estate management and estate purpose as distinct and separate from what is farming. I think sometimes that estates get into trouble because the two intermingle and you can't disentangle one from the other. Sometimes costs get piled on to a farming operation for other purposes that probably shouldn't be there. Separating the two and managing them separately is good discipline.'

Butley Priory Gatehouse: a comfortable home and guest house for its tenants

Close to the River Butley on the heathlands of east Suffolk stands the gatehouse of Butley Priory, virtually all that remains of the Augustinian Priory founded here in 1171. It was built under William de Geystone (Prior 1311–1322). The priory originally comprised a magnificent collection of buildings, and covered an area of 20 acres enclosed by a stone wall.

Sir Edward Greenwell, the present owner, let the gatehouse in 1987 to

Greenwell Estate changes over 25 years

	1977	2002
Livestock		
Dairy cows	200	0
Beef cows	1200	0
Sows	100	220
Arable land: approx hectares (acres)		
Cereals	500 ha (1,235 acres)	586 (1,448 acres)
Sugar beet	150 ha (370 acres)	177 (437 acres)
Potatoes	55 ha (135 acres)	236 (583 acres)
Field vegetables	45 ha (111 acres)	186 (459 acres)
Forage	50 ha (123 acres)	Set-aside 67 (165 acres)
Grass	400 ha (988 acres)	287 (709 acres)
Total area farmed by family	*1,200 ha (2965 acres)*	*1,540 ha (3,805 acres)*
Employees:		
Farming	41	15
Foresters	2	0
Gamekeepers	3	2
Maintenance	12	3
Office	5	1.5
Total	*63*	*21.5*

Ned and Frances Cavendish, who have continued the ongoing process of restoration to turn it into a guest house and private residence. Although little remains of this once great priory except the fine stone building and an arch which once led out of the south transept of the church, the plan of the site is known from the excavations carried out in 1930 by Montague Rendell, a scholar and former headmaster of Winchester, who bought the gatehouse in 1926.

Said Sir Edward: 'Dr Rendell devoted his everything to putting the building back into living order and to a certain amount of archaeological excavation, and I think he pretty much bankrupted himself doing it. He

*Butley Priory
Gatehouse, which Sir
Edward has let for use
as a guest house.*

lived for the rest of his life in the house, and my grandfather bought it to have when he died, which was about 20 years later, and so that is how it came into our possession.

'It is a wonderful thing to own, a unique building. There is nothing else like it. It has a magnificent vaulted room, the main room, which used to be open at each end and you could drive through underneath. Each side of that is a brick-vaulted room, on one side a kitchen and on the other a sitting room. You have to go up 48 steps to get to the first floor, where there are three or four bedrooms, and then you go up a further 28 steps to get to the next floor. The walls have a huge thickness, so that in some ways it is not the most practical of buildings to live in. Once you let it get cold in winter you are going to be cold until spring; vice-versa, keep it warm and you will survive.'

Unique features of the building are its extensive armorial frieze on the north side and exuberant flush-work decoration. The stone used in the building of the priory came from the valley of the Yonne in France, and was brought up the Butley river in barges. Sir Edward explained that like the building of some churches along the east coast, 'it was cheaper, presumably, to bring stone by barge from France across the North Sea or the Channel, along the coast and, in the case of Butley Priory, to just about the bottom of my mother's garden, than it was to haul it from a quarry beyond Cambridge, say 80 miles. Hauling stone across what were then the rutted tracks of East Anglia would have been such hard work. So they brought it from France where there were quarries on the coast.' A canal was cut to bring the stone to the wharf only 200 yards south of the priory church. The first king to visit Butley Priory appears to have been Henry III, who arrived on 9 March 1235.

It was Edward I who, saving himself considerable expense, billeted superannuated servants at monasteries, and sent Roger le Usher to Butley to be maintained in some style with two horses and two grooms. The record of this event, dated 1303, declares that he was an unwelcome guest. Notwithstanding, the King saw fit to send another pensioner, a Master William, in June of the same year, but he was sent back by the priory, who declared they could not afford to keep him, burdened as they were by debts. It appears that the King was most displeased and returned the unfortunate Master William to Butley where he remained until his death in 1312. Tradition has it that somewhere within the priory grounds is buried a silver coffin containing the body of Michael de la Pole, 3rd Earl of Suffolk, who fell at the side of Edward Plantagenet, Duke of York, at Agincourt.

It was during the time of Prior Augustine Rivet (1509–28) that the priory became the regular resort of many of the nobility who came there for the hunting. Mary Tudor, sister to Henry VIII, was a frequent visitor between 1515 and 1519. In 1527 she stayed for two months, accompanied by her new husband, Charles Brandon, Duke of Suffolk.

On 6 August 1527, as it was very hot, the former dowager Queen of France ordered her supper to be laid out in a shady part of the garden on the east side of the gatehouse. She so enjoyed the picnic that suppers in the priory gardens became a regular feature of her stays. It is recorded that in Brother Nicholas's garden the royal party were overtaken by a tremendous storm and had to rush to the church for shelter.

It was some time after Mary Tudor's death that on 1 March 1538 Butley Priory, with all its lands and properties, was surrendered to her brother the King. The commissioner who received the surrender, William Petre, stated that 'we have today received the surrender of Butley, to which the Convent has assented very quietly'.

For the next two years the priory was used as a royal hunting lodge before being granted in 1540 to Thomas, Duke of Norfolk, who in turn sold it to William Forthe of Hadleigh in 1544 for £910 2s 2d. Anne, his only daughter, inherited it and later married Viscount Hereford, who left

it to his daughter Elizabeth. She married John Clyatt in 1684 and having no children, she settled the estate on his children and heirs.

In 1737 George Wright Esq. married the Clyatt heiress and inherited the property. It was George Wright who restored the gatehouse and converted it into 'a handsome mansion.' Later the house became the residence or shooting seat of many important people of the day, including the Marquis of Donegall, Lord Archibald Hamilton and Lord Rendlesham. After this time it went into decline for some years and was used periodically as a very cold vicarage, until in 1926 the gatehouse was saved again by the aforementioned Dr Rendell, who called in the famous architect Caroe and began an intensive programme of restoration and re-conservation.

The larger passageway with its magnificent quadripartite vaulted ceiling was formed into the main reception room (currently the dining room). New panelling and a new fireplace decorated with heraldic shields were put in. A new front entrance was introduced into an angle of the east wing. Bedrooms and a bathroom were located above and a kitchen created out of the Georgian annexe. Buttresses were repaired and the armorial frieze was carefully conserved.

During World War Two, a landmine was dropped on the garden at the rear of the gatehouse, about 50 yards from the house. Landmines were designed to sink right into the ground, and when it exploded it left a perfect circular crater. The exploded material nicked the ridge point, and the beam that runs from the back to the front of the house was pushed right through and knocked off the front ridge as well. But Sir Edward considers himself lucky that his ancient building was not completely demolished.

Two years as president of the CLA 'a great experience'

My visit to Gedgrave in January 2004 followed shortly after Sir Edward Greenwell completed two years in office as the national president of the influential Country Land and Business Association, known to all in the rural community by the initials CLA. It was, he said, a great experience, though he admits that sometimes it consumed more time than he thought he had to give, and the position required him to 'go up a couple of gears' to achieve all he wanted to do on top of looking after things at home.

'One of the things I was very concerned to do was to define what the CLA was all about and to remind us of our role of protecting rights of property,' he said. This was interesting in relationship to life at Gedgrave,

The magnificent stone vaulted Great Hall of Butley Priory Gatehouse, where meals are served to guests.

Thomas Crisp - an extraordinary resident of Gedgrave and Butley

One of the earlier residents of both Gedgrave Hall and Butley Priory was Thomas Crisp, considered an extraordinary young man and among the finest Suffolk heavy horse breeders of his 19th-century generation. Following his death in 1869, the Suffolk Horse Society Stud Book records that 'in a notice of principal breeders of Suffolk horses, no name deserves a higher place than that of the late Mr Thomas Crisp.'

He had been for many years a breeder and exhibitor and his family, for three generations, had been celebrated for their Suffolk horses. The first Suffolk Punch of which there is any specific knowledge belonged to his grandfather. Thomas was of the third generation and was born at Red House, Rendlesham, but the family moved to Gedgrave Hall (described as being built of Queen Anne red and black brickwork) and Thomas was about 19 years old when the farm devolved to him. The record states that, at that time, Gedgrave Hall was 'a fine farm of 800 acres – essentially a stock farm, one which requires an intimate knowledge of what belongs to breeding, rearing and selling.'

During his occupation of Gedgrave, Thomas Crisp also took on Church Farm, Chillesford, and then Hill Farm in the same parish. In 1851 the executors of the younger Mr Catlin gave up Chillesford Lodge, and Mr Crisp then left residence at Gedgrave, hired Lodge Farm and went to live there for some four or five years. In 1855 the elder Mr Catlin died and when a new tenant was required for the priory, Mr Crisp went to live at Butley. For a time, Thomas Crisp farmed at Gedgrave, Chillesford, Butley and elsewhere – a total of some 4,000 acres.

When he died suddenly in 1869, his obituary reviewed his life in the most glowing terms: 'In the county of Suffolk the name of Thomas Crisp was regarded as an integral part of its agriculture. When mentioned at home or abroad, it was sure to be in relation to some marked event in the rural history of the county or in connection with some extraordinary farming feat of the day. As a breeder, successful exhibitor, or as an all round judge of stock, he was said to be the first in the Eastern Counties, but it was chiefly in connection with Suffolk horses and pigs that his name was known beyond.

'At the time the Royal Agricultural Society was in its infancy, he was a very successful exhibitor of Southdowns. But the Shorthorn fancy was never freely indulged in, although there was always a very quiet trade between the Butley pastures and the Continent at comfortable though far from sensational prices. The county never lacked a good tale founded on the doings at Gedgrave, Chillesford or Butley.'

'particularly with regard to the concept of property in relation to flood defence and defended land behind; whose responsibility it is to look after it, who may defend it and who may not.' He has succeeded in bringing this to the forefront of the association's activity for now, but Sir Edward feels that in 50 years time, the land may well not extend as far as it does today, if a policy of allowing things to 'return to nature' is implemented.

Sir Edward said that his time as CLA leader saw the beginnings of the biggest single change in agricultural policy in recent times, at least since the war, contained in the Review of the Common Agricultural Policy (CAP). 'For the first time ever we are going to be rewarded for looking after our land in an environmentally friendly way rather than for production,' he said. 'The effect it would have has not yet been fully understood, because people are going to sit back and ask: "Will I make money from farming this field to barley this year?" If I am honest with myself, I'm barely going to break even, and there is a risk of things going wrong and I will lose money. We might see, over the next two or three years, some quite radical changes in the way land is farmed; it won't have such an impact here in this part of Suffolk, because of the fact that we are already growing as much of the crops as we can outside the CAP – all the vegetables and all the potatoes, which are of course unsupported regimes – so we should not be so much affected by the Midterm Review. However, we might be affected because other people elsewhere will be tempted into crops that we are growing if they decide that cereals, despite this year's better prices, aren't, in the long term, very profitable to grow.'

During Sir Edward's time as President of the CLA, and before that, the organisation had started to acknowledge that its members' interests were not just in farming. 'Yes, they are owners of land, owners of built property, farmhouses, and so on, but increasingly, they are involved in businesses that are not just farming. Usually, almost always, farming is part of it, either directly or through a tenant or some contract arrangement, but a majority of landowner businesses now have something going on apart from the business of managing land.' The change of name to the Country Land and Business Association took place just before Sir Edward began his term as president, and being very keen on that happening he helped to push that change through. He hopes that the change reflects a truer image than the old name of Country Landowners, which he believes gave the public a false image of the membership.

The recent foot and mouth outbreak made people begin to reassess the rural economy, 'because they suddenly saw the way in which tourism – the biggest single discrete business of the countryside – inter-related with farming, and showed that people's enjoyment of the countryside was to do with the way farmers managed it.' At the time of foot and mouth everything, not just farming, went into cold storage; nothing happened at all. After that, there was the creation of DEFRA, something that the CLA had been asking for for 25 years – 'not exactly an instant triumph of lobbying, but at least we got it in the end.' It reflected that the countryside was a much more inter-related thing than had been thought previously. Since 1939 all rural policy had been seen as being delivered by agricultural policy and by agricultural grants. 'That's what rural policy was. But it has not been true for quite a long time now, and it has taken time for government to adjust its institutions to reflect that.'

Bibliography

History of St John's Manor, John and Pat Knock, 1997.

Reprint from *The Archaeological Journal Vol. 145,* for 1988, The Royal Archaeological Institute.

An Historical Atlas of Suffolk, Suffolk County Council

Index